REMEMBER
THE
ROSES

by
Irene Y. Rahmer

A Hearthstone Book

Carlton Press, Inc.   New York, N.Y.

REMEMBER THE ROSES

June 12, 1971

Darling, the birthday bushes are so beautiful, white orange blossoms, showering their sweet scent at the front door and by the driveway. The red roses in front of the house are so alive. The locust tree and the maple overhang the yard, newly mown by the near neighbor who always said "my roses" when you talked of yours. How you went back and forth valuing each other's flowers and comparing grasses! The bare space in front of the big window is now prayerfully planted with little yellow marigolds. "Oh, God, help them grow and bloom. Whisper to me how Harry did it."

Your old white hobby jeans fit me well enough, and your tee shirt is not too baggy. Nobody apparently watched me work outside except Mrs. Christman, who called to me about the sore toe I had mentioned to her a few days ago, but I didn't remember I had toes. The earth felt good on my hands, and the water cooled the plants. It was eighty degrees outside. I am almost happy, but I suppose that's just the frosting on the cake.

I waver between being almost happy and utterly bereft. I know I am emerging from that strange dreamlike grace of God's peace and calm which shrouded fears and enabled me to carry on with an automatic courage and a sense of rightness for the decisions that needed to be made. For so many years I could talk to you of trivial things or more important ones, and you always listened. It was one of your many charms, the fact that you always heard me. Now, who do I tell it to? That, I think, is the greatest loss, that and the nearness and the touch of you. Who, who do I tell it to? Like an owl in the darkness of night, I call. Perhaps in some strange way, unknown to mortals, you still hear, and in the same strange way send courage and love to bridge the chasm.

There was a party today at noon, and yesterday there were two parties. Central High women teachers, thirty or forty, went to the country club for lunch. There was good food and good talk, and Mrs. Watson told us how it was in New Mexico, where she has bought a house in Roswell. When I get ready to go anywhere, I always want you to pass inspection, to approve, to zip me up, to touch me maybe. That I hunger and thirst for. But I think I looked pretty, and I know everyone else did. That helps. And Mrs. Watson's enthusiastic talk gave me courage. She is making it alone, apparently happy—her four children scattered, her husband long gone. I still remember the look on her face, after she had come to work at Central High, when one day in a confidential moment about her widowhood she said, "Just think, no one will ever kiss me again."

At the Good-by to Central party yesterday, I sat with Mr. Baughman for rolls and coffee. I was called up first for recognition. My dedication to teaching, my inspiration to others, my love of beauty were mentioned by Mr. McFadden, department head. In response, I simply said I was not much of a speaker, but that I wanted to say one thing, "Harry and I together have totaled ninety years in the teaching profession—that's a long time for both of us—long enough for a lovely arch of rainbow remembrances." And then I said my thank-you for the retirement gift—a twenty-five-dollar certificate from Ayres' Store. Mr. Yager and Mr. Baughman, the other retirees, were called up front for their recognition. There followed fun and sentimentality and good-bys. Now, no more Central, teachers and pupils both out of the central city and into outlying area schools.

Outside there was climactic thunder and rain. Mr. Baughman took me home to get my raincoat and to rest a bit before it was time to go to the other party. He went to a paint store—he will have to paint houses for seven years until his wife retires from an insurance company. At the appointed time, he honked for me, and we were off to the next party at Baer Field Inn, where all the retirees from the city schools were honored. Mr. Teeter, the school-board member across the table from me, was in school in New Castle when Mr. Baughman was the principal. We all talked a lot, got pins, certificates, praise, and final checks. Back to the Lincoln Bank in the rainstorm, Mr. Baughman remarked that if he had been a girl, he would have been a prostitute. "The best bragging I ever heard," I answered. But how sweet it was to have him help me not to feel so lonely and lost at those two parties! How good to have a man help me into my raincoat!

Oh, I almost forgot another party—the usual yearly one celebrating the June eighth birthdays. Walter and Lucile, Terry and Marcia, and Grace and I had a wonderful supper at the Four Winds. Helen and Dave didn't drive up from Muncie, so three of the original six were not present. That made it very different from last year. You and I had the supper at the Carousel, the original six at one table, and the two young couples at the next table. You were the perfect host, seeing that the young were happy and doing your bit at our table. You were genial, radiant. Later, at the house, there was the birthday cake with candles, and ice cream, candies, nuts. But Dave gave out and had to lie down to rest. I put him on the studio couch and threw a blanket over him. We didn't want him to make the drive home, but he insisted. He was the one who remarked the last couple times that one of us would break up this group before too long. Well, Walter had made the reservations and we were given a big round table in a pretty corner. But there were seven chairs. I saw Grace look at Walter, and he quickly edged the extra chair to another table and started arranging the remaining chairs and telling us where to sit. The vacant chair is everywhere—but I must not see it, or say it.

June 19, 1971

Darling, I came home from my brother's house with Florence and found Mr. Nahrwold mowing the lawn. It cut me as much as the grass, not seeing you there as usual in your old garden togs. I talked to him and appreciated him, and he showed me where the roses needed water. The thermometer in the garage said ninety-five degrees, so I went into the house and turned on the air conditioner and felt selfish and blue. I want to hold you so tight! I got the evening paper off the porch, fixed a noodle and chicken broth supper, with vegetables, Nellie's peaches, and a pot of coffee. It was hard to eat alone—you loved my noodles, and the coffee—oh!

Then I read the evening paper. Hayakawa's essay on "Life That Is Forever New" was so beautiful. All emotionally healthy people are creative in their own way. There are many forms of art—a good marriage, a novel way of presenting arithmetic, a rose garden. The relation between all things changes from day to day in a subtle stealth of change. The act of bringing together the uniqueness of yourself at the moment with the uniqueness of your materials at the moment and the uniqueness of other people's feelings at the moment—that is creativity, whether the end-product takes the form of a painting or an original casserole dish. And for the creative individual, living, like art, is also forever new.

Did Jesus say something like, "My task is easy, my yoke is light?" Anyway, I was surprised at how light the seventy-five-foot hose was, even with the addition attached. I found Daddy's web chair that he was so proud of, and I spent the evening in the garden tending your roses. Old Mr. Melcher came out and I knew he was lonesome, so I went to his white picket fence, and we stood and talked about his tomato plants. We talked about you, too. He is eighty-six, just the age Daddy was when he left us.

I used to think "my husband and my father," over and over when there was so much illness for both of you in the '60s. But somehow we made it for awhile, and I am glad for the experience and the goodness that grew in my heart as I erased some of the hurt. Now I can help neither of you, my men folk—my so very close men folk. And I am a man's woman.

When Mr. Haley, one of my favorite principals, stood at your silver casket loaded with red roses and the still harmony of you, and when he put an arm about my waist and held my right hand in his and talked of courage with the lovely lilt in his voice, then I knew again that I was a man's woman—though forever yours—and that I could find courage and loveliness and harmony, as you would want.

As I was watering the last of the roses, a lone firefly crossed and recrossed the hedge and the mock orange bush. Was I silly in playing with the thought that you were praising me and promising to light the way?

June 23, 1971

Darling, you've been away twenty-six days now, and sometimes I think I can't stand it another minute. I loved you so, and I remember the two kisses I put on your warm forehead when alone with you a minute in the hospital room before the doctor came. Do you remember how you kissed me twice on my left cheek just after the marriage ceremony? Those kisses always stayed. We had said, "till death do us part," and now, fearing the ceremonial end, I wanted to return those kisses. They will stay, too!

Sometimes I think there's a conspiracy to keep me from re-

8

membering. My sister urged me to substitute at a bridge party in the Liberty Mills Addition. The houses were modern, like pictures, and the one we went to was red brick with white columns. Inside were lovely antiques, refinished by the owner. The lady of the manor was in the hospital with a bleeding ulcer and other troubles. There were twin boys, nine years old, but they were away while Grandma entertained. We had refreshments at one o'clock and then started to play bridge. But my mind wandered—I wanted to fly into your arms in our little cottage where the roses grow. Even so, I came out third high among the women.

This morning I went to the clinic and paid the last fifty dollars on your doctor bill. I left the insurance blank and have all the receipts lined up to turn in. I am trying hard to take care of things. I watered your roses again and cut off tulip leaves. I washed your pajamas and your underwear. I am not sure what to do with those things, but they should be used again by someone. I mailed the notes to the pallbearers finally. They had pretty, blurred roses in a delicate pink on them, and I tried to write a neat message. I shall have to write to your principal later. It hurts too much—I can't do it yet. You and he were so close, and he has always been so good to me. You, and Doris Hansen from the same school year! And the same way! She was only fifty-four. I can see you yet, so strong and healthy looking, talking to her husband by the closed casket.

My mother's birthday is tomorrow. She almost made her seventy years. I wonder if I can. Daddy made eighty-six. The tears are coming finally. What my parents went through in their last six years! And what you must have gone through in the last six of yours! But I never admired you more than in this last year. Did I tell you? Sometimes I think we both felt it coming. You were so good to me, and I reached for you so often—for old folks—or were we, as they say, young at heart?

I have studied and thought a lot about the car. I must learn to drive it somehow and get a license this very month.

June 27, 1971
Darling, I went to the chapel today before ten o'clock. It was empty, so I put my hand on the back of our preferred pew and looked at the red and blue window and prayed for the week, a week as you might want it. I thought my thank-yous: a thank-

you for our joy as you sang so gloriously beside me in the church, a thank-you for our sweet love life, a thank-you for our work together, a thank-you for our struggles, a thank-you for our always coming together again after a difference. Oh, God has been so good to us! Then I went on into the big church and sat alone in a short seat, but I wasn't exactly lonely—you are so much a part of me—and we in God, and God in we.

I went by taxi to the chapel that first Sunday in June. Your fellow usher took my hand and said consoling words, and my hand brushed his coat sleeve in parting. Oh, the magic of a man's sleeve, of a man's arm. You and he were so handsome together as you seated people and took up the offering and presented it at the altar.

Helen Burr has been picking me up and dropping me off at my church on the way to hers. When she came to my church for me today, she found many people to talk to, so I went on in to McKay Hall for some coffee. As I cooled it with cream, there was Jean, my sister's sister-in-law. She didn't know about you, so we talked and felt like sisters under the skin, widows, Helen finally got talked out, and we came home in the heat to Baxter Street. I feel the dinners should be mine, out somewhere, or here at home.

This time I had dark red roses and blue delphiniums on the table. Soon there was steak, carrots, lettuce and tomato salad, with strawberries and angel food for dessert. We had picked up a pan of muffins at her house, and I baked them—so good! She has been with me so often through so much. Since 1937 I have known her.

When she left at three o'clock, I was not ready to be alone, so I called Florence and Ken to come for supper. Had the fish dish you liked and big strawberry sundaes for dessert. I thought of you many times later in the evening, and of how my sister and her husband helped me as you left on your journey. I like people, but at times I like to be alone. You were people to me, and I could be alone happily with you.

Last night I was eating crackers and milk before I went to bed, as you sometimes did, in the dinette chair by the kitchen door. All of a sudden I thought I had spilled milk on my hand, but it was water—from my eyes, unconsciously. Did I ever say, "I just want to be me. Let me be me?" Or was it something from a Sammy Davis song?

June 28, 1971

Hi, Honey, just a month ago was your last full day alive. I kissed one of your red velvet roses on the table twice the first thing this morning. It was soft and fragrant, so sweet, like you.

I did odd jobs after breakfast because Ken was coming at eleven o'clock to fix the light on the front porch. Florence phoned after he had started to tell me to lay off that "Joe" stuff. I forgot and called him Joe last night, and I guess Ken must be jealous of her friend of so many years. But I heard her call Ken "Harry" recently. I hope Ken doesn't get confused.

I got a call from Mr. Holt's secretary saying the $10,000 check was there, and asking if they should mail it since Vivian was on vacation. We talked about the medical and hospital bills and about the pension papers Mr. Ferguson will have to fill out. After I was through talking, I thought of the money and heard myself saying "God Almighty." Again I found myself kissing the rose and felt hot tears spattering my hands. Somehow, some sense got into my head, and I realized that one of us was bound to have to pick up for the other—that is the way it usually is in a marriage.

Downtown I went to the courthouse to get a copy of our marriage certificate for the teachers' retirement fund requirement. Wonder what the hippies and free lovers and common-law people do? Maybe they are less involved. Would that be better or worse?

But we were married at Simpson M.E., a little, gray stone church around the corner from where I roomed. The minister, Rev. Adams, had preached in my home town in his youth, and in yours later. Only his wife and the organist, and the happiest couple we knew, Ruth and Fritz, were with us. We trampled crisp autumn leaves as we four friends walked the two blocks to the church about four o'clock that October afternoon. The altar was beautiful with palms and ferns and white mums and candles—there was to be an evening wedding—and our simple one had the benefit of all that loveliness.

I hadn't been able to find the dress I wanted. Everything was to be brown and gold—but the only dress that would do was soldier blue. It was October 26, 1944, and there was a war going on. Anyway, I felt pretty as I dressed, with ten-year-old Joan Hirons looking on. And when she cried because I was leaving her home, I told her I'd come to her wedding. She became a teacher, and later we did go to her wedding. The new suit you had ordered

11

didn't come, but you were very handsome in your best old one. We were so happy at last, my ring was five diamonds set in platinum, and we knelt for a prayer and said the Lord's Prayer together, and then were declared man and wife, and kisses and congratulations and picture taking followed. The shining band on my hand held a tiny diamond for each year from 1939 to 1944.

And the dinner for Ruth and Fritz and you and me at the Berghoff Gardens was exquisite—we started with Bacardi cocktails, and followed with mignon fillets and baked potatoes and salads. Afterward Ruth and Fritz left us, and we peeked in on the teachers' convention by way of the back stairs, and then you carried me over the threshold of the upstairs apartment we had been getting ready. And it all became as the old song—sweeter as the years go by—through our teaching and our illnesses and our quarrels and our travels and our trying to get ahead.

Always, always, I loved you—and always, always, you loved me. We thought we had something pretty special. No matter what, there was that strong undercurrent of affection moving us along toward eternity. Always, you held doors open for me; now, it was given to me to hold the door open for you—you first.

I took my driver's test, and I wished for you to pray for me as you did in the room below where I took my master's exam at Columbia University. I passed with ninety-five percent—now I must drive your new beige Nova with the pretty green interior.

Tears are falling on my bare bosom—my slip has slipped. As you would say, "You might as well laugh as cry." Or, "Now, now, it's not all that bad." But it is, because I want your arms around me, and I want to kiss your dimples.

The telephone rings all the time. Before supper Ben Roth, who was in Florida, called. Honey, he didn't know you were dead till today! And the cemetery man called about my grave. Both of them talked for a long time. And I called Wayne Brown, and also Jon about going to Europe. Wayne can't, but I hope Jon can. He has been a wonderful nephew, standing with me through the funeral, and since.

June 30, 1971

Hi, Harry, I did a term paper tonight. The attorney told me to get your bonds evaluated and list them with serial numbers, face value, and the date. He said it would be done by customer service at the bank, but the bank lady only wrote the value of each bond, and she said the attorney's secretary could do the rest. The attorney said he didn't want the bonds floating around the office, that I should do it! Five pages of ink-written figures. But you did very well—you invested $9,750 in 1952 to 1963 and ended up with $15,016.08, over $5,000 in interest. Then there was the regular payment of thirty dollars on the house we bought in 1950. Bless you, the regular savings gave you a measure of wealth, and we were happy making our house a home together.

In 1952, you were forty-three, and I was forty-seven. We were over our operations. You had surgery, and nine months later, surgery again. My two operations were six months apart. But we were on our way again. You had lost your father, and had left Garrett to teach in New Haven. I suppose those "bond years," 1952 to 1963, were some of our very lush years, though Mother died in 1954. In 1960 Daddy's troubles began when he was eighty. In 1964 your trouble began with your heart attack, but you climbed a high hill. I guess, as Longfellow says, "Life is checkered shade and sunshine."

I went to your grave today, and for a new one it looked nice and level, with a good name plate. I gazed and gazed at your name. I have always liked it—Harry W. Rahmer. The grave is in a pretty place, I think. It's on a low hill with a tree, and it looks across a winding roadway toward a shallow green valley. And your good superintendent, Mr. Harding, is very near—you were both sixty-two. Anyway, I paid for my lot and checked about a headstone for the two of us. Yes, I am taking this trip, too.

Venetta and I went to the I.U. meeting about Europe after supper together at the Hobby Ranch. Previously I had spent an hour with the attorney. Yes, I am going to Europe. I hope the plane has a good engine, or rather, the planes. Since you can't be around to clear up some things, I want to do it for you.

Darling, the humbleness and the defeat of life keep getting mixed with the pride and lushness. I was so proud of you so often, and yet I shall forever see you in your tee shirt and pajama bottoms, lying on the basement floor at the feet of the Master. Help me. I thirst.

Nellie called. Mamie is depressed, Minnie goes to the doctor for her blood pressure. I know your sisters all ache with missing you.

Jon came and took me to Mr. Ferguson about your pension

papers, and then I drove the car in the cemetery. Jon taught me so much in such a little time. Oh, honey, this isn't the way I thought it would be, without teaching—without you. Oh, I could sit in the shade and be sad. But I know you wouldn't want me to be a cry baby. I'll put on a gallant smile and maybe I'll really feel gallant. It will never, never be the same without you. I loved you, really loved you. Maybe this is a wrong thing, a morbid thing, I am doing—this thinking in writing. And then again, maybe it is a release, a rightful way of facing reality. Perhaps, because for a little while I am true to self, I can better go on with the show. At least there must be some balance, some rhythm that will merge with the meaning God may be insisting on. "Lead, Kindly Light, the night is dark, and I am far from home."

July 1, 1971

Hi, Harry, just one month ago today, June 1, was the last time I looked on your face. As I left the cemetery, it began to sprinkle, and then the rain came in torrents. Oh, how it rained that afternoon and evening! I kept wondering if your grave was closed yet. The undertaker let me out at the house, and Jon, Ken, and Florence went on to where their cars were. Lloyd left—he had been at the house all through this. I just wanted to be alone. Later, Florence and Ken took me to Hall's Stockyards for supper. How good the steak and baked potato and salad tasted! I don't remember eating at all after the breakfast the nurse brought me at the hospital. I suppose I did find food in the refrigerator.

It is very hot and dry now. I cut off dead roses late this afternoon, and weeded, and watered. Things don't look as perfect as you would have them, but I am trying.

I think I am moving into your room tomorrow—did a lot of straightening. This study has been my room since December 24, 1964, when you came home from the hospital after your heart attack. I think we both liked the set-up. You had been in the hospital since November 11. I didn't want to crowd you, and my doctor said I should let you reach for me. Now, I think it unwise to have an empty bedroom. This can be a pure study then. I am going to try to keep the yard, the house, and myself pretty.

Jon forgot his glasses yesterday after my driving lesson and came back, so I asked him to take me to the Credit Union office and then downtown. I went to the attorney with the bond sheets

14

and to the banks to collect interest, but there wasn't the usual thrill. Far from it! I felt like a thief or a robber with your money, mine or Uncle Sam's. Yet we had everything we wanted, or were we too busy to know what we wanted? As you warned me, I'll try not to be foolish with your money. I just don't want to be foolish about anything.

I must watch and not talk too much about my loss of you—I must not make others uncomfortable. Maybe I can sweep up the heart and put love away. I got along before I knew you for some thirty years. And then there was that night in New York when we stood and looked out my high window at the myriad lights, and somehow I felt the tremendous fear and joy and the burden of the moment. Nothing would ever be the same again—we would look together at life. You didn't kiss me—there was just the awe that you would many times and that I would be ready. How can I ever sweep that moment away? And yet, and yet, perhaps that is what sweeping up the heart means, taking another good-by look.

July 2, 1971

Hi, Honey, I thought this date would be too overwhelming and that I couldn't write, but all day I have worked as if it were Saturday—at the beauty shop I learned it was Friday. So since I seemingly have another day in the week, I can write. In 1940 you came to New York by train, tired, on this date, so tired you were having double vision and a headache. I can see you now, asleep on the big-flowered cretonne spread on the studio couch. I sat in a chair and watched you, watched the lines go out of your face, watched the vital glow of the waves in your red-gold hair. It was almost too much to fathom, the love we seemed to have, after the pain and suffering of other loves for both of us. You and I alone in New York—our friends had finished at Columbia, or given up—we would get our master's degrees—the last lap. A married life, a teaching life!Thirty-one years ago, when you were thirty-one—now neither. Some know not what they have until they have it not. We always knew.

I got busy on the house as soon as breakfast was over. I am moving into your room, which means I had to do a lot of juggling. It is better that way. The room became so beautiful after I worked on it. I stood and stared at it several times—pink is cheerful—like roses. The studio bed in the study is now a davenport. There is more space. I bought a light green blotter for the desk. It is a roomier room now. I must find some pretty pillows. Oh, I cleaned and cleaned; it hadn't been done since the day Florence and I did the whole house as best we could that fatal day in May. Some of your things are going out, some will be used by others, and some will be kept. But I have to sweep up, I have to live here awhile. Later, I don't know.

I keep thinking you prayed to go because you knew it was a heart attack or a stroke. And you were helpless and you couldn't talk right. I almost know you would pray to go. And if you prayed, why should I go against prayer? In the hospital, your hand pressuring mine maybe was reassurance that I would get along, knowing that you showed me you loved me as long as you were able to. Remember, at supper that night, we sat hand in hand after we had finished eating, and then you pulled me up, saying, "Let's lie down awhile, an hour or so." And then at two-fifteen you came into the study laughing, saying "Guess what time it is. We really fooled ourselves on that hour!" You looked so rested. Your sleep was out, you said. Could you make a pot of coffee? Could you wash the supper dishes? Could you pack the wash? Would you keep me awake? "Heavens, no," I answered as I got up and stumbled around and then went back to bed. "Nothing would keep me awake."

Then, "Irene, Irene, Irene, Irene, Irene," echoed in my brain, from the depth of somewhere. The basement! Thank God, you got me awake. Thank God, I tried to get help. I was so frightened and I worked so fast. It was three-fifteen. You didn't want me to be away from you, but I had to get the doctor on the phone, and the four policemen came quickly. And then the nurses, and the two doctors at the hospital. Finally, a black nurse with heaven around her, sitting with me and holding your things, and the two ministers. One had said a prayer with "leaning on the everlasting arms" in it; and the other, Rev. Amstein, took me home in a funny little gray car, a VW, I think. It was funny because he was so big, and there were so many freckles on his face. I never would have guessed our minister had so many freckles. We stopped to look at your garden, all perfectly ready for sun and rain, new rose stubs still showing. Strange things, like the minister's freckles, stand out in grief that is just beginning.

In the house the minister sat in your place at the table and talked to me. Then he called Mungovan's and the newspaper. And I had to talk to Woodie so your three sisters would know. And I called Florence and Lucile. The minister left sometime after we decided when the services would be, and every question seemed answered. It seemed as if it were a re-run, as if I had lived through it all before, somehow.

Now it's midnight, and it's July 2—that day when we were again together in New York after three weeks apart. Five weeks ago, we laughed and joked at 2:15 a.m. I go to your room now and to your bed.

July 3, 1971

Darling, I don't understand—I am almost happy this evening at ten-thirty. I woke up sharply at eight this morning rested, and refreshed with canned grapefruit and waffles and a pot of coffee. I sat in the chair by the kitchen. I don't like to use either of the ones where we sometimes held hands after supper and chatted about the school day. It was so beautiful out with the locust tree gently waving, showing a pure blue sky in the west. I dressed and went out into the garden. Wasn't it funny how we always ate breakfast in our night clothes? Well, why not, if they are pretty?

The garden was nice—it still needs more know-how—but it is pretty good. Those rose bushes at the end of the fence are doing well. Oh, the blue of the sky as I looked up for the hint of a cloud and found none!

I walked to the laundromat and checked about having a washing done. At the grocery I shopped for bread, milk, and bing cherries. I noted the possibility of dry cleaning; there was a beauty shop, a gift shop with a post office, a dress shop, a shoe shop, a drug store, a bank. What more could I ask as an un-driver, and only five blocks away? I came home and carried as much as I could of the sheets, towels, and your tee shirts to the laundromat. I could go back in the afternoon to get them. As I walked home, it seemed that you were loving me and patting me on the back, using that certain tone that accompanied, "You are the most loved woman in Fort Wayne."

Open the door and let me go. "Lo, I am with you always." God in you, and God in me, and we in God. Attunement. Humph! Happy with the spiritual you rather than the physical, the mem-

17

orable you rather than the reality you. I don't know. As William James says, I think, "putting on a front" will help to create the fact. Shakespeare in *Hamlet* says something like "assume a virtue if you have it not." But Christ says, "as a man thinketh in his heart, so is he." I know how my heart feels, and, frankly, I am frightened, my feet unwilling to travel the way they must go. Yet I must "get on my gear and go."

An old song says, "Open wide the door, let a little sunshine in." Does it also say, "It's the sunshine makes the shadow, as we know?" I have had so much sunshine with you, the shade is hard to take, this last shade. In the back of my account book is written, "All sunshine makes a desert." A line from a long-ago movie comes to my mind in which Ann Harding says, "Out of my way, out of my way, I've got work to do." So much goes on inside my head, but maybe I sleep better and feel better if I let my thoughts surface.

July 6, 1971

Darling, Helen Burr and I hurried home from Monroeville tonight to watch *Portrait of Jennie* on TV. It was lovely and reminded me of us—hot chocolate in New York the first time we were alone—in a long narrow restaurant with red leather booths and shiny black tables. Oh, the wonder and uncertainty of the first hints of love, and the promise of it; and at the very end, the loss. Tears peaked out, I was so far beyond tears at first. I may be meeting them on the way back.

There was so much mail, a card from Lucile, a letter from Miss Lucasse, an insurance check for $2700. I whimpered, sometimes I find myself making moans. Sounds help, I guess.

The good life we had so much of caresses me exquisitely, and then there is the torture of Poe's raven saying, "Nevermore." Tears and whimpers must go—I must seek a higher life, a higher realm of life. I don't see how I can go on sanely otherwise. I am so scared sometimes. Eating is no good without you. Looking pretty was all for you. Yet I must find the way as others have.

You know, it's strange in a way. For some uncanny reason this past school year I kept a picture of Catherine Marshall just inside my middle desk drawer. It was a picture on a sunny yellow background, and each time I came back to school, after having a substitute, I wondered if it had been noticed. When I pulled out your similar drawer at your school, there was a yellow circle in the identical spot with "smile" in strong black letters. Does it mean, "Face the sun, and you will cease your sad repining?" Catherine came through, I think, with a smile. The minister had a sermonette Sunday for the children about a plant that was saved by the sun.

I sent Danny the handkerchief I bought for you in Zurich last summer. I wrote a note with it to him and Woodice. It was so very pretty, and I felt you would approve.

I know now what my father meant when he said Sundays and holidays were the hardest after Mother died. I have been at a low ebb over the Fourth. Yet Marilyn and her girls stopped in; Helen Burr took me to the Hoekstra's in Monroeville tonight, where we stayed for supper. And we visited Ruth Whittern, who is also going to Europe this summer. Life must go one, but how I ache for the feel and the presence of you.

July 7, 1971

Hi, Harry, I feel so much better tonight. I just have to talk about it. Jon came in to give me another lesson in driving. I got some of your things ready to take out for him and Lloyd and David: combs, shirts, belts, socks. I also left the laundry at the mat." After talking a little with Lloyd, Jon and I started my lesson at the school building. I drove for forty-five minutes to Monroeville and around, and then back to near the Wayne Trace where I gave over the car. Jon drove to the CharKing where we had lunch together. Three of his bosses from the Harvester were there, and one of them talked to Jon. Maybe he will soon be back at work, and I will lose my teacher. Jon and I went to Florence's awhile.

I took your insurance check to the bank and went to the lawyer's office to report some things. I paid the final funeral bill. Came home after getting a sympathy card for the Crowe girls and some lemons and strawberries. I watered the roses and the other flowers until eleven tonight.

Mrs. Nahrwold came to talk to me, about us, about other people like me, about living. Also, when I was downtown today I ran into Margaret Wiggs, who is going to Europe, too. Her husband will be gone two years in October. Yesterday was his birthday—she kept so busy, drove to Muncie. The love and the loss have stayed,

19

but she is so vital and so encouraging. Her husband fell downstairs and died instantly.

Strange things happen—God moves in mysterious ways. As I was driving our car with Jon this morning, another was tailing us. It went around and stopped on the berm. Seeing it was my brother, I went around and stopped on the berm ahead of him. He came over to my side of the car and thrust a book, *Beyond Ourselves*, by Catherine Marshall, in to me and said, "I want you to have this. It did me more good than anything else." His wife and Jon's mother. I have read the first eighty pages, and it does help.

Nothing can bring you back. I have two simple alternatives: to have a good life listening for God's plan, or to have a miserable existence, a moaning experience. And I know what you would choose for me. Therefore, I choose it too. We were happy together, we understood each other, we believed that life was more interesting if we were not too possessive, if we each allowed the other freedom. So it is freedom, the freedom of life and death, and togetherness in memory, togetherness in knowing that your will for me would be my will not to cling too closely.

I hope I can treasure the joyousness that fills our home as the hour nears midnight, a midnight that must have a very round golden moon somewhere, because it was coming up in the east while I was watering the roses. But when I put the hose away, I forgot to glance for it.

July 14, 1971

Darling, I have just counted the days, forty-seven of them, more than twice as many as separated us when I went to Europe last summer. Sometimes I wonder how I can go on without you. I hope you fully realized how much I cared, and I think you did. You always carried our wedding picture in your billfold.

I keep hurting about the six upper teeth you had left and the milk and little cup of peanut butter you had for lunch, and a lunch time of less than a half an hour. Of course you had your coffee. And I tried to give you a breakfast and a supper and a before-bedtime snack that you could manage. One by one, your teeth went, especially the top ones, and there was always dental surgery. Everything that hurt you hurt me, but oh, how I admired you for managing—and the vacancies didn't show so much. You were proud—it must have been difficult.

The attorney went over things with me today, and I signed papers, so many. An estate of about $100,000. To have you back, I'd toss it all and start over. We'd make it—maybe you could sell or tend roses, and I could cook or make salads. Of course, you could teach. You were proud of being a good teacher and of saving so much money. Of course there are taxes and taxes. And I have been driving your car illegally. The attorney gave me papers to get the title changed, and there's a new sixty-day waiting period instead of the old thirty. It means no car or driving lessons until July 29. I could get tangled up badly if I jammed someone.

I talked to Harold and Helen, and they do lock their garage—to keep kids from partying in the car after bedtime. Mr. Krauskopf came over and fixed the garage lock and advised about the windows you said needed puttying. I planted some volunteer salvia in an empty space back of the house. The roses look better. I see so much to do everywhere I look. I went through the desk drawers pretty thoroughly tonight. I want to get things in order before I leave for Europe. I went to a resale store today. I do not know quite what to do with some of your clothes. Mr. Thomas, the tailor, will try to sell that last two suits, what is left of the one.

I wrote to Shirley last night, from the heart, about your sisters and the way they seemed to take things—against me. I read the six pages over and over to check if I wanted to mail them. Someone in the family should understand how I felt and what we wanted. If that doesn't help, then I am at a dead end. But rest assured, I will remember you and try to come through with what is right. I shall watch for any leads.

The wedding was July 10, Mike and Val. Lots of people at the church. Jon and I took care of Roger's girls in the afternoon before the very fancy reception and the luncheon for the wedding party and closest relatives. We six enjoyed lunch at Atz's North and then went to Holiday Inn East, where a swim party kept Jon and the girls splashing while I enjoyed a deck chair and my memories of other weddings in my sister's family. She is getting ready to be a great grandmother—there's the one who caught two bridal bouquets in the past month coming on, too.

Helen Burr and I went to church the next day and out to eat. John Bardon came in the evening. He has a lot of problems—has quit his job, and is thinking of another.

Yesterday was the annual party in Decatur with Margaret and Helen and Florence and me. It was enjoyable. I bought a white dress, an easy care one with gold buttons. Saw Mildred Niblick, and later we four drove past the house where she and Harold live. The church bought up houses around it for a parking lot and an addition to the church. Harold wouldn't sell, so his house looks like a sore thumb. I guess one has to swing with the times.

And that reminds me, I must swing a little better, my spontaneity is drooping. Two weeks from tomorrow I will be in London, and I have got to liven up and install some gaiety. I think you would appreciate a lighter step, a quicker one.

July 15, 1971

Darling, I am your widow. It says so all over the attorney's papers, and that word has always bothered. Widows seem so forlorn—maybe it's all in my head. Mother and Dad were so happy—his arm was usually across her when we went into the bedroom from little on up. Then when we went to high school, there were Mrs. Holmes and Mrs. Schamerloh, who boarded us—their men were gone, and it was sad to me. There is a term "merry widow," and I might as well be merry. You would have it so, I know.

I missed you tonight when I needed to make out papers for a visa. You would have driven me out to South Town to a photograph machine. You took me so many places and you seemed to enjoy doing it. When the attorney put his arm about my waist today for a minute, and I felt the strength and life from it, I missed you. You were so clean and sweet and warm and gentle. The other night I lay in bed and thought of your body, your arm beneath my head, your feet against mine. It was a sort of reverence for the goodness of you.

At the hospital, at the end, as the doctors were working with you, your feet were uncovered and I was holding the ankles, feeling the pulse beats, which beat on after your face had blued, and I thought how clean your feet were, every toenail. I didn't see how it could be the end, with your pulse still beating, but the doctors said the part of the brain that controlled breathing was paralyzed, and the heart would have to stop—your heart, my heart.

Every day now I am getting ready to go to Europe. Bought two new girdles. Talked to Venetta on the phone. Have the lower cupboards in order. Must check the top ones tomorrow, possibly trim the hedge with Jon, get out to I.U. to see Joe, get to the banks to transfer accounts, and get my hair fixed. Time will go, and it may ease the hurt, though if I let myself be natural, I don't see how.

How I loved sending you cards last year and bringing you a Swiss watch that I let no one else see till you saw it! And you always had time to kiss me hello or good-by; even when I was on the cart going to surgery those times, you bent over me to leave your love and your comfort. I wonder if I left you enough this last time, or if I was too practical about getting help and not moving you. I keep seeing your cheek on the cement floor—why didn't I put something soft under it?

Dr. Popenoe said in the *News* there were only four sufferings: pain, fear, a feeling of guilt, and loneliness. If I let myself, I can claim them all as I think over life with and without you. But one of your school pictures brings me far more cheer and humor than I ever thought it would at the time. I am so glad there are two of them—there is so much "come hither and we will see what we can learn together joyfully" in them. Appeal and winsomeness abound as your dimples seem to deepen—but it is a strong face, too. That's why I said yes. You had both feet on the ground and you made me feel safe and secure and sound. You tempered my mercurial meanderings.

July 17, 1971

Darling, our doctor is married again—his wife has been gone almost two years—and they are off to Hawaii. She was a Mrs., and they will live in his home. Aren't you glad? He must not be fifty yet—he and his two girls need a mama.

Half a hundred days have gone by since my mouth pressed your forehead in good-by. Oh, how glad I was to be with you at the last, to be what help I could! How I ache to come home from town and find Mr. Nahrwold mowing the lawn, but I suppose I would ache more if I didn't have him to help and advise me. He is going to the hospital after Labor Day—hernia. I got busy today and hoed around your roses and watered some of them and trimmed the faded blooms.

Being a widow is bad—but never having been able to be one would be much worse. As Tennyson says, "It is better to have loved and lost, than never to have loved at all." I suppose married people are uncomfortable around a widow—she is such a reminder to both—if they love. I can think of nothing worse than to "pair off" or "company up" with single women for any length of time. I am a man's woman—as my father was a woman's man. And I am not particularly attracted to people my age or older. Now just where do I fit in? "Oh, come on, let's jump into the car and drive out to Atz's for a lemon soda and a turtle sundae!" you say.

I did a fool thing today. I lay down on the cellar floor where you lay May 29 at 3:15 a.m.—for how long you lay calling me I know not—and my cheek was on the cement and it was cold. And then a longish bug went scurrying by my nose, and I got up fast.

I straightened three closets somewhat this morning. And I put my blouses in your plastic shirt container in the basement and brought your few shirts left upstairs. I took two unused tee shirts back to Patterson Fletcher's and they refunded the money.

Yesterday I was downtown from 9:00 to 7:00 getting pictures and papers for my visa to Hungary, observing reading classes at I.U., talking to Grace and Joe, and all afternoon I had bank books changed and also the Lincoln Life annuity. When I came home there was a letter about your teacher's pension. As you always said, you are leaving me well off financially. And you are leaving me with rosy memories—so many. And as I always told you, "You were the best-looking man there, and the sweetest one to nestle up to here."

July 20, 1971

Sweetheart, I don't see any reason to lie or pretend—I ache so at times with missing you—and I say mentally, "Why me? Why me?" In the basement as I was getting ready to take a shower after Jon went home, I let loose until I sounded like a wounded animal, and I held the warm washcloth against my eyes that won't cry right. I don't ever want anyone to know. I don't want them to be uncomfortable. But you, I can and always could tell anything to. It was always so good to come home to you.

Jon came in at 2:00 and we trimmed the hedge and the dead roses and the mock orange bushes. And what a lot of weeds I pulled! I wore your old white putter pants and a tee shirt.

After he left and I got cleaned up, I went to Maloley's for fruit, bread, and ice cream, but first I ate at the counter at Gardener's

24

between two married couples. I had eaten at Ayres' at noon. It is not easy to sit down to eat alone at home.

I took your clothes, the latest ones to Thomas to sell—they are too good to give away or junk. And I went to the American Federal to get your account changed to my name. Tonight I mailed a consent to transfer to Defiance. I talked to a man at the Fort Wayne National Bank about the insurance checking account. I must get a C.D. or something because I am losing about three dollars a day in interest.

I opened a sack to put some garbage in tonight. and there was a note from Nellie. Remember the night she put a sack of candy in our car and we had it to eat on the way home from Garrett? The wrappers were still in the sack. She was always giving us something.

Oh, Harry, on that basement floor, you thought of your principal first, and then of your sisters. I tried to do my best in my great sorrow, but I guess I came out the loser—the in-law. "Oh, thou soul of my soul! I shall clasp thee again, and with God be the rest."

No heaven on this earth was ever like clasping you. It eased all the turmoil and the trouble of those years before and in the thirties. Was it the same for you? I think from the tenderness and the sweetness of you, it surely was. And we never gave it up.

Only I think you asked God—I think you knew how a stroke might leave you—and you did say it was a heart attack or a stroke—but you thought the latter. So maybe you asked that I might not have a greater burden—so maybe, out of your great love for me, you gave me a freedom that I should sing praises for. And maybe I do not walk alone—maybe in spirit you and God are with me. Maybe I can get myself "squared around" to accept more completely the new dimension.

You went to the chapel at 8:00 for us from New Year's on—there was a resolution not to miss a Sunday. I slept until you came in looking so handsome and with a sack of donuts for our coffee. And you always told me who was in church and other morning news. I havn't missed a Sunday since you couldn't go.

Since it has to be, I feel good about you being on the hill where you are, where I shall be in time, beside you, beside you, dear.

July 21, 1971

Where are you, Harry? Where, oh, where are you, Harry? That is what I mixed with your name as I called it ever so many times from the gold chair tonight. Momentarily I felt I could not exist another minute without you. But one can call so long to seemingly unhearing ears, then one can only try to cry tears until reason returns. It is the lowest ebb of sorrow. And one wonders if there should be a tomorrow.

Venetta, Florence, Ethel, and I went to see Aunt Etta at the Davis Nursing Home today after a good dinner at the Dutch Mill. Almost twenty years older than you and with reason wandering, she lives on. Her nose looks healed since the cancer surgery. She has life but what is it worth to her or to humanity?

As women will, we shopped then. I bought beige silk house slippers with rosettes, and Venetta and Ethel found shoes and dresses.

Venetta and I took Florence home and then came here. We visited until 7:30 and then went to Cardone's new restaurant for Italian salad, wine, pizza, and coffee. We talked about the hospital, our coming trip, and many other things—you, too. Oh, Harry, nothing will ever really be right without you, no matter how I kid myself!

Our togetherness, our teaching life, and so much is gone. Your sisters will never be the same to me. It may be wicked to lament when I still have so much. My wedding ring, the silver and the dishes with the rose design, the rose garden, this comfortable home, your new car, all of them were so wonderful with you to share them.

Like a bolt out of the blue, like a thief in the night, like a trite phrase in eloquence was your death to my life. There are so many adjustments to make, alone. In the main, we are all lonely creatures—but in happy marriage, we are less alone than in any other relationship. You told me once that when I wore your ring I would feel a security I had never known before, and it was so true.

Oh, honey, I will get some sleep and be so thankful for what I have got, and tomorrow I will go on doing the things you had to leave undone. I will try to keep well and sane. And I will try to keep sweet and pretty and young. You would not want me to lose my sparkle, so I shall try to add gaiety to wholesomeness. *Try* is a good-sounding word. It is forward moving.

July 22, 1971

Hi, Harry, I am sitting in a clean house—worked all day on it—and I thought of you so much because we have done so much cleaning together. The Eureka outfit you bought before I went to Europe last summer really got a workout. I first changed both the sweeper bag and the canister bag, and it was not as puzzling as I imagined it might be. Oh, it was so wonderful to accomplish so much!

I paid some bills and figured your pension. It did not seem right, so I wrote to Indianapolis about it. Kept feeling that you would dash me to the post office in the Nova when it was ready—but I walked to the shopping center. Came home and pulled out some crowded zinnias where you had your little seed bed. Also I reset some marigolds where I wanted splashes of yellow instead of bareness. I noticed all the roses, and I puzzle over what to put on them. There is so much stuff in cans and bottles, and some of it isn't labeled. It is so hard to try to figure out what to do about some things.

I thought of you when I made a good strawberry sundae for supper, and at noon when I fixed some of Liechty's roast beef and gravy on mashed potatoes. You were so easy to cook for. I get a lump in my throat lots of times when I sit down alone to something you liked. I suppose I will always see that chocolate chip ice cream in Dad's mottled yellow and brown dish, and the two chocolate graham wafers I put on your napkin that last night—a last dessert.

One week from tonight I will be high in the air away to London, but I won't wear your farewell kiss—yet the sweetness of you is fast in my mouth forever, those last two kisses on your warm brow in the hospital.

Sometimes I get to wondering if death is the reality, and life, the dream. Did I dream some of the things I write about? Will they recede as Charles Lamb's "dream children" did?

I suppose I need another house to clean, or a coconut sundae. Might as well get rid of what little coconut is left in the blue bowl.

July 25, 1971

Hi, Harry, sometimes I think I can't get it all through my head, the fact that I will never see you again. I just looked at your pictures in the envelopes on the desk, and in three of those I like best, taken at different ages, you look happy. But were you happy enough? Is anyone?

There was a young blond minister, a Mr. Wray, who is interning, I think, preaching this morning, and he was so intense in his message about Jonah's anger and about God's ways and about what we can do to further them. As he talked at the chapel service, I could not help thinking about your wanting to be a minister twenty years ago.

I tried then to point out all the perils—you had just turned forty and we had bought this house. Yet there was a teacher at North Side High School who quit teaching at thirty-eight to become a physician, and he is now a very successful one. I suggested that a teacher could really be a minister as he worked with youth, and that one could do church work without being the minister. You did get into helping with the pledges and ushering. And you had such a good singing voice. And your bearing had so much dignity. I sometimes thought you would have made a good doctor. Anyway, I told you if you really wanted to be a minister, you could study at Union Theological in New York, and I would teach there or here and see you through. We would make it. I remember talking to Bob Thompson about it when I rode to school with him. But somehow that desire which seemed pretty strong at the time got sidetracked. I know you were religious—you used to go out early from the motel in the morning and put your hand on the hood of the car and pray for a safe day of travel. And you told me how you felt early in the morning among your roses.

Florence and Ken took me to I.U. for the final meeting about the European trip. After it was over, Venetta, Grace, and I ate at the North CharKing. Then Venetta and I went to the Avalon Church at Waynedale to hear some Hawaiian singers, one of whom is working at the hospital and attending the Bible college. Rather, he joined them. There were about fifteen, mostly young women, some who had become Christians from a Buddhist background, and they were very good. In story and song they touched my heart and made me think of you, and what your enjoyment would have been, too.

I am going to try to savor this trip. I don't want to fake an enjoyment and I don't want to make others unhappy with my sadness. I hope a true enjoyment of God's world and his people wells up within me. I hope the greatness of having you with me thirty-two years can overshadow the torrent of loss and loneliness that seems to increase instead of decrease in these nearly sixty days. I am glad you don't have to bear it, if you loved as much as I—and you may have deeply loved, even more.

Catherine Marshall ended one book with her and her son taking a boat out on the waves—after her husband was gone. She ended another with her mother thinking about getting a young boy to help with the farm work—after her father died. Can cheer and work and looking ahead balance the sorrow and puzzle of looking back at our togetherness? How can I ever forget the touch of you, the concern of you, the security of your presence? And should I?

I went around and looked at all the flowers after I came home about 7:30. The far bed of roses, east of the bedroom window is of all shades of pink—and I know you made that for me because I told you I thought a rose should be pink, my favorite color. There are so many other colors other places, and the zinnias are better than any others we ever had. I held a lovely yellow one in my hand, and there were such precious tiny ones that volunteered along with the mottled ones I set out. They are doing quite well with the recent rain and perhaps with the dusting I gave them. The tulips this spring were so lovely—I am so glad you got to cherish them. Ethel's coral-colored geraniums and the yellow and maroon marigolds and the tiny salvia are so pretty. You loved flowers and you loved your home. You must have loved it dearly. When I come back from Europe, I shall brighten the corner where we loved as much as I can, inside and out.

Now I am going to get the check you wrote at Christmas, for my trip, and put it on the chest near your Columbia diploma and your picture that was taken when you were forty-two, that age when many men are most attractive. Thank you. Thank you.

August 26, 1971

Hi, Harry, it is good to be home again. One week ago tonight I was in the big plane coming this way fast. Jon, Marilyn, Cathy, and loving Amy met me and took me to Ken and Florence's where his birthday cake was ready to blaze—a little party—so it wasn't too lonely. Later the young people came in with me and stayed a bit here. But after they left, how I wanted to throw my arms around you and feel the security of your embrace! It would have been heaven, as it always was.

Just now it is difficult to write because I have clipped so many dead blossoms and pruned what needed it. I worked more than two hours and powdered the roses, all of them. I must count the bushes sometime. I sat down to supper and couldn't eat afterward, so I got up and went into the bedroom to look at your picture with the flags on each side, flags from Roskilde in Denmark. We were married during a war, but you were not taken then. I rubbed my eyes and came back—my coffee was just right.

Your lovely nurse, Venetta, and Florence and Ethel and I went to the Bluffton Nursing Home to see Aunt Etta, who was pretty clear—she knew us and sang a church song for us. You wouldn't have wanted to be bedfast—but does she? Your way was best. I bought a new dress on sale, but who-for, what-for?

I looked at your contract. Ordinarily, this would be your first day of school, and I would eagerly await the news of New Haven. That way retirement might not be so severe—but it is double, retirement from school and from marriage—two very valuable and happy ways of life for me. I shall keep on driving the car with Jon's help—to Grabill yesterday and to Hoagland today. I shall keep straightening things out and discarding. I shall try to get the business in order. I shall try to plan some fun things and keep up appearances.

Oh, honey, the Europe you gave me was wonderful! I can't begin to tell you what memories I have of London, Copenhagen, Vienna, Geneva, Madrid! Four or five days in each, enough to feel the pulse of the city! A rich, rich gift! Thank you so much! You have given me so many things along with the tenderness and the warmth and the security. It is awfully hard sometimes to forget to remember, so truly was I blessed. I can never block it out. I shall have to live mostly in the present, hope for the future, but each day, just a little, I must think of the goodness of God in giving me you.

Long ago when school was new to me, I mused over a pussy cat rhyme about London and the queen. I did see the queen's palace. And I marveled at the charm of Ingrid Bergman from a front seat of one of the theaters where she was in a play by George Bernard Shaw. Truly a queen! I walked where Shakespeare walked in the beautiful countryside on a clear day. In Copenhagen, Venetta and I walked the length of the Stroget, along with hundreds of others, right in the middle of the street, stopping now and then to enter a shop or gaze at a window display. We went to Tivoli Gardens three times, so exciting did we find the flowers, the fountains, the amusements, the food, the fireworks at night. I felt most at home in Vienna, that lovely city of music, of St. Stevens Cathedral, of Maria Theresa's Schonbrunn Palace. We went everywhere, walking or in taxis. We sat at a sidewalk cafe with beer and long sausage buns, followed by heavenly squares of cake. In the largest, most beautiful cemetery, we stood beside the monument of Beethoven taking pictures and talking, or trying to talk, with a homey native woman, her son, and his college friend who could speak some English. In Geneva, Venetta and I, with fresh Swiss hairdos, tasted our first goblets of sangria in a cozy restaurant at noon. In the evening, there was a boatride on Lake Geneva. In Madrid I bought lovely folding fans for your sisters, and as a souvenir I found a sapphire ring, the color of the Spanish sky in summer.

We were often with Hope and Welcome, two sisters. Hope had married Phil just before the tour. I was attracted to Bill Hart, a young widower, and his daughter. He is a teacher of creative writing at I.U. Then there's Big Joe from I.U. Geri Boldt and Bill Maxfield were planning to be married, the second time for both of them. Hope's husband had been killed in an auto wreck. These new friends, and many more, will dance into my life and thoughts often. Scenes and happenings will revive and thrill me to the end of my time. There's a frame of reference for reading, listening to music, looking at beautiful pictures. Thank you. Thank you.

August 27, 1971

Hi, I am more at peace now—for awhile today I thought I would burst any moment. The telephone is out for three days now—I missed my driver's lesson—I saw so much to do—there are so many preparations in the basement that I do not understand, for flowers, soap, cleansers, etc., in so many various containers. But I did feel better when I had my hair fixed.

Do you remember the Dickens Room at Marshall, Michigan? There was such a cozy evening once when we came in out of the cold after a long ride, you and I and Howard and Marguerite. We were seated near a burning fireplace, and you men faced us women. We were forty, forty-two, forty-four and forty-six, old enough to be young and gay. You fellows had beers and we had cocktails—the dinner was terrific and we were all aglow, enjoying the interval before the long ride home. Marguerite and I sat in the back seat, where we still are. You were sixty-two with a sheaf of red roses in May, and he is sixty with a sheaf of yellow mums in August. I said good-by to him—he went quicker than you, at 12:30 a.m. on the edge of his bed while she was calling for help—tonight, and I said what little I could to Marguerite. Close couples can be so rich in living. Now death has taken three of every close couple group we ever had: Howard, Ed, Agnes.

It is wonderful to be supremely important to someone, and to be needed, and to have the audience of fellow workers dealing with youth, and the audience of youth. To be seen, to have an image, to be appreciated—is that a widow's lot? Or is a widow's lot best next to her husband's?

I pray that God will guard and guide me in the time I have left, so that I am worthy, not worthless. I must seek to be a self, not a wife, not a teacher—a self. Perhaps there are other values than the ones I became so enmeshed, so engrossed, so enchanted with. There is no time to fritter with fears and tears. I must be gay enough to attract and give gayety again. I can sit and rock only long enough to think of something to get up and run for, or sense something running my way. Like Tennyson's Ulysses, I must set sail, other adventures to seek.

August 30, 1971

Darling, it was three months ago yesterday—and I am beginning to know people are not wanting me to bewail in speech any more. Down town I saw Mrs. Stackhouse, who used to teach with me before she married her doctor. She was still telling me about when she lost her minister, and I could tell he was first in her heart. But I sensed a subtle door closing when she reminded me that I would go over and over some of our happenings—but that after awhile they would be lovely memories. My hairdresser said to a remark of mine about you—yes, many, many, times you will have this or that as an anniversary. And then there is a silence sometimes if I forget and say something and use your name. It must be as Kipling said— "and never breathe a word about your loss." I shall have to live in the present with others.

Yet, tonight might have been heaven. You would have come home from your first day of school, and I would have enjoyed all the New Haven news after I had fed you. We would have had the house in order, the roses would not be struggling so, there would not be the worry of my driving, or the settling of the estate, or the mulling over so much that is puzzling to me. A school year just as a housewife for you! How I should have loved that! We liked our way of life, and we never would have been ready. And I know it would have killed you to be pushed in a wheel chair, or to have lain an invalid here or in a nursing home. Someone has said, "The saddest words of tongue or pen are these—it might have been." So I will do with what is and try to be happy.

In *Good Housekeeping* I read something about how important touch is in showing love. There is a woman who is forever touching me, and it is so repulsive. I try to avoid it. I am a man's woman. But the touch of you, even your feet against mine, was so pleasant. The touch of you, the sight of you, the sound of your voice, all of these were music to my soul. You were so clean. And how you and I enjoyed tasting our meals together! I suppose I should go and fix a cheese toastie and a cup of coffee.

I wrote Mamie a card and mailed the fans for your sisters to her. Nellis has been ill a month with strep throat—talked on the phone to her yesterday. Saw the lawyer and checked on Social Security and driving school.

The new minister is huge. Helen B. and I were at church, at the MCL for dinner. Lucile came to bring back the orange sherbet I left in their car Saturday night. Venetta came to watch Henry VIII's wives on TV at 8:30. Poor, poor old Henry—he loved Catherine Howard but he couldn't consummate that love. Oh, there are so many things I'd like to talk over with you—now that I have time and it is too late for you. Venetta had an older friend, a former minister, who died suddenly, and she and her mother went to the funeral Saturday. He wrote to her while we were in Europe. I fairly ache to confide in you and to accept your help.

Now then, a most important day of my retirement is at its crisis, and I must do many things, remembering to smile into the mirror sometimes. A beautiful story in *Good Housekeeping* ends somewhat thus: And in my silent soul I scream out . . . past the windows—the skies—and the clouds—and whatever goes past that into the great incredible, unbelievable forever, and I cry, "I love you, I love you, I love you."

And back it comes, softly, sweetly, full of that familiar laughing grace—"Why, honey, don't you think I know that? . . . Don't you really think I know that?"

September 4, 1971

Oh, Harry, I thought most of the day that I couldn't make it alone. It was almost the worst day I have had—and I worked awfully hard to keep ahead of the lump in my throat. Florence took me to the store, and Helen B. and Olive Perkins phoned. But school is starting and you and I are not going, and I ache so for you. I need you so with every need a woman has for a man. The sight of your empty coat sleeves when I opened your closet nearly killed me. I rubbed my hands across them all and closed the door and went on sweeping, yes, sweeping and weeping. I worked until 3:00 on the house, then I took a bath. After supper I went out and dug dandelions and weeds and picked off black-spotted leaves from the roses. I tore up some zinnias that were mildewed. Sweat dropped off me, and I remembered I had just had a bath, so I went into the air-cooled house and washed a bit. Then I paid the taxes, the church, ordered the grapefruit, looked over the papers on the desk. It will be one-hundred days tomorrow that you have been away.

Honey, there is a cricket yelping in the basement. I turn on the light and go down to locate him, but he sees me first and calms down. He has been there some time, so he has kept me jumping. I saw him tonight for the first—he's big and fat—and I got one of your shoes to whack him with. I missed him, perhaps because I think I have heard it is bad luck to kill a cricket. He went back of a tile and I yanked the tile away, and a can of Air-wick deodorant spray fell out of the tile, I shook it and pressed the cap and it sprayed. Now what do you think of that? Was that fat cricket trying to tell me I had missed one?

I will just have to explain later how I don't know what I feel—I think I am hungry. Anyway, I am hurt and lost and bewildered, but one thing is sure—the sight of you and your arms would cure it all.

September 7, 1971

Hi, honey; never will I forget this day—the first day of school in forty-nine years since I started teaching—and I was not there. I left the house shortly after 8:00 and went with Frank Forsyth

34

to select your marker—a deep rose stone like your beloved superintendent has. I kept feeling you ought to be helping me, and finally I saw a faint R dancing in the grain. Mr. Forsyth saw it too in a certain slant of light. Do I believe in signs?

Took my first driver's lesson on an automatic transmission. Perhaps that is what I should have, but I hate to part with the car you chose and liked so well. Went to Social Security for Florence and Ken—phoned her at Roger's in Milwaukee. They are off on a three weeks' vacation in the West and will visit his folks in North Dakota and Montana. Ate at Ayers'. Home and cut down the old zinnias. Mr. Nahrwold went to the hospital for an operation. Was lamenting to myself about the lawn which needs mowing. A black-eyed boy was going by with a mower, and I hailed him. Sure enough, he would mow my lawn for two dollars. He had a good start before I saw there was no catcher, but I was glad to get the grass cut shorter anyway.

Phoned Lloyd, and he wanted me to see Gerry's marker and eat supper with him. So we went all through the cemetery at Hoagland and on down to where he had made such an improvement on Grandma Van Horn's lot. We talked a long time and he brought me back after supper past Florence's house. I gave him some of your things for him and David. I just have to discard, and I hope it was all right.

Nellie wrote and sent the last picture taken of you, me, Woodie, and Bob around the Easter table. It means so much to me. She was glad to get the fan from Madrid. Mamie wrote to thank me for hers. Both said how much they loved you and how hard it was to accept the way it is. Minnie called from Steve's house and thanked me—said her fan was the prettiest—said Shirley is pregnant again. Thank you for "tipping me off" about getting them something in Europe.

Lloyd said he would never forget you standing at his door when we were leaving after Gerry's death. You said, "I'll be next." I tried to cancel it out, but he said you fingered your keys and looked knowingly serious. Both of us loved both of you very much. You know, I believe I wore the same navy and white to both funerals. Lloyd and I talked also about Dad and Uncle Willard who went in '67 and '69. I was so ill those times with flu and you were so very good to me. It scares me to think of being alone with winter coming on. Margaret Wiggs has weathered it and gave me inspiration today to keep kicking.

September 9, 1971

Hi, Harry. I listened to Billy Graham last night and tonight as he talked in California to thousands, and I think you would have enjoyed him or been touched by him, too. He spoke of "loneliness" last night, and of "earthquakes," even personal earthquakes such as the loss of a loved one. I let the tears fall down as I missed you so, and as I resolved to go on as you would have me. I even knelt on the white rug by your bedside. Honey, I could always tell you anything—and I never wanted to hurt you, even though I must have sometimes. I was afraid for you to smoke so much and to drink so much coffee. Did we quarrel about much else? When I told you to bring me a "permit" from your doctor, or else go live with Nellie, if you insisted on smoking, you simply became quieter and moved underground.

After I came home from the hospital that Saturday, I noticed the grate on the drain awry, and as I went to set it aright I found a freshly crunched white cigarette just inside, the last thing you must have been able to do before you lay helpless beside the grate. I haven't told anyone. Then later I found part of a package of cigs on the little southeast table back of some things, and in the garage there was part of a package back of box. I lifted a shoe down from the stack of paper towels and it had a lighter and a can of butane in it. The net became full of lighters, fuels, matches, mouth washes, aerosols, and deodorants. The strange thing is that the latter three must work. I did not know how much you were smoking, but so many people told me afterward about seeing you with your coffee and your cigarette at various places. Some said you asked them not to tell me. I am not exactly happy about this smoky secret life, but it must have added some adventure and spice. No wonder the nice red leather chair came to the underground, and no wonder you shined so many shoes and fixed so many things in the basement. There were all those strategic points of protection. Well, some people have had heart attacks and strokes, who never thought of such gaiety, although I wasn't very gay as I, time after time, came across Cepachol, Brisk, and Scope. And when that cricket yelped the other night and I moved the tile and rattled a can of Airwick spray, I wondered what more might be around. Humanity hath its weaknesses. I wonder what mine are?

Whatever they are, and whatever yours were, there was, I am sure, a togetherness that was treasured by both of us. As I wrote that line, I felt a reassurance, a loving reassurance, surround and enfold me, almost as if I were taken in arms, almost as if we were holding each other for a long minute as we so often did. "Put me together again," I sometimes called it because it steadied me so.

Goodnight, sweetheart, I can drive better tomorrow and sleep better tonight since I have confided in you.

September 11, 1971

Hi, honey, this would be the end of the first two weeks of school, and I suppose your check would be tucked away. We would be very happy because I have not missed teaching, much as you thought I would. Of course, I had a driver's lesson every day and a lunch at Ayers'. But, holy of holies, the dream suppers with you, and the nights. The hope I had to be just a housewife for you instead of for me!

Nevertheless, I picked up, here and there, all day, inside and out. Honey, in the garage in that bucket of paper towels I found a lighter and a bottle of mouthwash—just below where I found the cigarettes back of a box in June. You really had the amunition at every strategic point. The big fat cricket that yelped in the tile where the aerosol was is dead, and I forgot to carry him out today. But then I did so many things in addition to a big personal wash.

Also I finished *The Condor Passes*, and it is very good—the wild urges of life are portrayed so well. I may want to reread some of it. The dream marriage that failed, the wild "wedding night" of the sister-in-law, and the old man's desire and ability fading at the same time made me think of many people and events. Oh, how I wish we could still share books and excerpts, TV programs, school affairs, people, and the gladness of just holding each other. Weekend nights! It all went so fast.

But I think I can be less forlorn living in the moment, looking upward, filling in some expectations of enjoyment, along with the study and the quiet that is very apt to surround me—but it must not engulf me. That is why I dressed up, ate at Gardener's, and shopped at Maloley's for food. I will drive the car when there are not so many neighbors around to watch me try to get into the garage.

Tonight is Miss America's night—so I shall watch loveliness and cast my votes silently. I am remembering a Miss Universe program in Sacramento in 1960. You went across from the motel and got a box of chicken and french fries and other goodies—it was quite cool out—and we ate in our room and watched TV. We crammed so much into our years together. The western sky is a brilliant blaze of color through the locust branches of the tree you planted. I must rush to gaze at it as it burns!

The dry-cleaner has been on the porch with his paper every evening. I wonder if he sees me go to the window. The rest of the sky overhead is full of rainy-looking clouds. Mr. Nahrwold is at the Lutheran. Oh, I'd like your neighborhood talk. "The hours I spent with thee, dear heart, are as a string of pearls to me . . . Oh, memories that bless and burn . . . I kiss each bead unto the end . . . and there a cross is hung . . . my rosary, my rosary."

September 18, 1971

Oh, my darling, another week has gone by. I cried so hard last Sunday night—it seemed I couldn't make it alone. Helen B. took me to church early, so I went to the coffee hour and visited with Ruth Fleck and some women. They talked about carrying food in to lonely sick people like Dr. Short. Cleon joined us.

Helen cooked dinner at her house—good corn-on-the-cob, cooked tomatoes, ham and green beans, etc. Then we went with Elma Neaderhouser to the Town House "open house." It was full of old ladies, alone, brave, I suppose—but somehow waiting. One of them mentioned Dr. Short—again. Ever since I was twenty-five, he has helped me to recover from bouts of kidney and bladder ailments. Now he's old and going. Came home about 5:00, and oh, how I wanted us together!

Took two driver's lessons, but the doctor says I can't do it anymore—have to watch my neck to save my numb three right fingers. I even drove out to Lloyd's and Marilyn's alone, but I couldn't get the car into the garage. The postman did it for me. People are kind. The dry-cleaner's wife said they would always take me places I had to go.

Nellie had been here when I came home Monday. She had looked at the roses and left a note in the mailbox. I saw how they looked from last week's heat and the grass was so tall. So I got busy, trimming the dead flowers, cleaning black-spot leaves, watering, weeding. Mrs. Nahrwold helped me with the mower, and I did the whole lawn. It looked so pretty the next day, and

I didn't feel like crying. Buds began to pop, and roses looked as roses should.

The week wore on as weeks will do, and I got through without you. I kept working on a poem that somehow got finished tonight, *The Wedding Band*. I don't know how good it is, but I finished it, as I mowed the lawn, as I drove the car alone. I boxed up all your ties and belts and handkerchiefs. I moved everything yours out of the bedroom closet. It is so hard to push your things out, but I am glad I didn't rush it. Walter and Lucile came in one night—had wanted to take me to Ye Old Inn, but I had eaten at Gardner's.

Honey, today was a wedding day for Geri Boldt and Bill Maxfield, people I learned to know on the European tour. Venetta and I met at 10:00, shopped, ate at Ayers', picked up Grace and went to the Messiah Lutheran Church on the Stellhorn Road. It was lovely! Bill's young roommate in Europe, Charles Lauer, was there. A second marriage for both. They told me their stories separately in Europe. They are honeymooning in Denver—right now there is six inches of snow there. Honey—if—if we could just go back to Denver in our little white Studebaker again; if—if we could have that many years ago, I'd make life a heaven on earth for you. I wasn't too bad, I guess, but we were both temperamental sometimes—you always said we got along better than most people. We were busy, we were sick, we were tired, sometimes.

Helen B. is taking me to church tomorrow, and after lunch we are going to see the new City-County Building. Venetta is coming at 4:30 and we are joining two of her friends for supper, then she and I are TVing ("Guess Who's Coming to Dinner") here while they go to church. It is almost 12:00. People are kind. God is good. God!

September 21, 1971

Oh, Harry, this is the last day of summer—of the first day of autumn—I couldn't settle. Went to the hospital for traction and for lunch. Then uptown to look around and came home with moth gas for our closets. To the Shell station about looking after your car, 1524 miles on it since April 7. To Maloley's where I bought quite a supply of food. Outside to look at the roses and the yard and to see what it needs. There is so much I do not understand, but I shall try to puzzle it out. Mr. Nahrwold pushed his mower a bit.

Honey, I don't know where the thought came from, but every single marriage, every single one almost, ends as ours did. You love along, you live along, and then one is alone. Somehow the thought gave me comfort. I tell myself I am sorry for you, cut off so quickly, but maybe I pity me more. I only know I feel so sorry you fell alone in the basement; and what defeat you must have felt, unable to get up on your feet—but still you could call for help. And I won't have you to help me, or will I? In Spirit.

I reached out in thought to my brother and my sister many times today in my restless mood. Tomorrow I go with Lucile to a retired teachers' meeting. If you were here, I would not go near it. It seems I take more time to do less and less. Without you, it all seems pointless, but I must remember your pride in appearances.

September 22, 1971

Hi, Honey, I suppose this is the first day of autumn—it was cool and beautiful. At 9:20 I was on my way to see Dr. Kachmann about my "arm" problem. The x-rays seem to show calcium deposits in my neck bones, which he says he can chip away if necessary. Five more treatments may stretch the space where the nerve comes through. Enjoyed the walk from the bus to the hospital area. I thought on the way home I'd go into the Alpine, where I used to breakfast in 1937 to 1940, and get a donut and coffee, but the donuts were gone and the place was not one bit nostalgic, so I excused myself and left.

Lucile picked me up to go to the retired teachers' meeting, and it was a little better than I thought it would be. Marvoline was there with shorter hair and wearing a green pants-suit. I am not too inspired with the word "retired."

Came home and mowed the front yard before the mower retired. Mrs. Nahrwold came over and talked and tried to help me, but to no avail. So I fixed some of your chunky beef soup, and then I went out again and cut off dead roses and hedge shoots. Harold and Helen are on vacation and have furnace problems at the lake and here. They are also painting the garage and fixing things. Oh, honey, I miss you, and how I miss the things you did to keep our place in shape. It is difficult for me, and I really don't know

40

how. Iva Spangler stopped and admired your roses.

When I came in, my eyes lighted on a November, 1939, *House and Garden* that I had brought up from the basement. A boy at school said his mother had saved it but thought I might have use for it at Central. It has pictures of the movie, "Gone with the Wind," the setting at Tara, and other pictures of southern plantation homes. Instantly I thought of the time you took me to the Embassy to see that movie. You were still very new to me, and I was so proud of you. Dr. Porter was there and spoke to me—and later he was so close to both of us. And when you were ill the first time, he went every noon to see you at the apartment. Then, when he died, you were so hurt—I can see you yet here on the davenport. He was sixty-three. Almost similar circumstances, in age and in that he practically crawled the block to his home when he was stricken and died the next day. But "Gone with the Wind" was so exciting, and so were you. And afterward we joined Dave Hartley and Flo at Throp's. What an evening! What a date! And in the deepest, truest part of my mind and heart it was always that way—living with you. Darling, I loved it! You gave me so much.

Those trips and visits to southern great houses in Natchez and other cities were so lovely. The culmination of dreams from reading Civil War stories, and the culmination of dreams that I might know the love that words suggested! My cup runneth over! Truly I have been blessed. I wonder if I gave enough?

That time when Dr. Porter said he could promise nothing in regard to your first operation, I left his office and turned against the brick wall outside and cried so hard. And Marilyn came along and pulled me to her and asked, "Why, Aunt Irene, whatever is the matter?" How could I tell her I couldn't live without you? Not really *live!* But you made it! We had twenty-two years more, in spite of other illness, mine as well. Truly I have been blessed. And I do believe I helped you and showed my appreciation and love enough. I could hardly wait to get to you after school—and I did get you good meals—and we were comfortable together.

I seem to have twice as much to do now. I hope and pray for the strength to "weed out" things we both can't use anymore, to keep up my own appearance, to keep up the appearance of the house and the yard, to keep an outflow of interests also. There are many like Marilyn who, although they don't reach out with their two hands, are concerned and compassionate. Truly I have been blessed. So, come warmth and spontaneity and generosity and awareness, there is life to be lived, and love to bequeath.

A picture of you at Lutheran is emerging, and your voice "Irene, I've enjoyed living with you," just flashed into my mind from Nov. 11, 1964.

Where the need is, God's gift is.

September 23, 1971

Hi, Harry, there's a chill in the air, and I just pulled the shades to shut out night and turned on the heat. I heard the back door at Helen's house. Never in all the years I was married to you did the charm of your coming home dwindle, whether you came in the back door in your church clothes, your black jacket, or your garden togs. The thrill of your light cars curving around the corner and into the garage was a hint of heaven. And it was a hint again when I came in and found you in my chair or yours, or on the bed, or in the basement, or at the card table grading papers—or perhaps looked out the back window to see you working with the roses.

I awakened with a severe neck ache, three numb right fingers, and a mad right toe. But an amazing amount of work chased them away after a waffle and coffee and fruit salad breakfast. Took the three weeks' laundry to the mat and had to walk back for it at 1:00. Cleaned the bedroom and put my personal wash away. Mowed the back yard and trimmed the unmowable places. Had the car taken to New Haven and washed and checked. Swept the garage. Threw out some stale plants, and put a light philodendrum into the orange kitty vase you liked. Talked to Lloyd, the neighbor Rabers, the postman, the Nahrwolds, and, of course, the two fellows who took the car away and brought it back. Have to keep talking so I don't get like Uncle Willard—who talked to his dishes, his eggs, etc.

The tax bills came. Oh, and I put the car in the garage alone. The boy, a former student of yours, just stood in front and guided me a little. Maybe I did put it in once when Jon did the same. Next time I will really have to do it alone.

After the work was done, I cleaned up and decided to look pretty while I listened to the 4:30 news and then got supper. Then I decided to read the *NRTA Journal*. It is such a strange, new world still, this being me instead of you and me. The thoughts one has time to think when one has retired from a career and a marriage! And no matter how busy one can force onself to be, they will not be silenced entirely, and perhaps a natural free flow is healthier. If rein is given to that within, perhaps that which is without will interfuse, and the result will be an emergence of a stronger, happier ego.

Acceptance, appreciation, aspiration. Three words moved in here. "Sinkers, floaters, swimmers." Three of your words moved in quickly. Yes, dear, I am trying to swim, all by myself.

September 24, 1971

Hi, Harry, my neck really hurt this morning, but the therapist fixed it—no looking at ceilings, skies, no twisting far sideways, and a very minimum of driving. Feel much better tonight, some finger numbness and tingle.

It was cool and pleasant walking to the hospital in my brown and white. Ate at the Paramount Grill, full of so many memories that were pleasant. How proud and happy I was that time after the bout in 1964 when we were finally able to get the corner table at the foot of the stairs, and we were living socially again! And Walter and Lucile came in and joined us. On leaving, I decided to walk in the sunshine past 3109 Hoagland Avenue.

And there it was, my home for three school years. It was 1937, my first summer out of Columbia, when I was guided by a filling station man who overheard my phone call about a place to live, to that square white house, so strong looking, so beautiful inside. The son was an artist, the pretty red-haired daughter later was my good friend Christine. It was all so wonderful—my green walls with silver stars, the gray and pink and purple rug, the big brown bed with a lavender spread, the full-length mirror on the dresser, the gray comfortable chair, the lavender-flowered floor lamp. There were Venetian blinds and a door to a balcony which I opened in spring and fall.

In three years I knew much success as a teacher, new friends, heartbreak, illness, summers at Columbia, and then you, so fresh, so sweet, so clean! My mind has just mulled over those sweet stirrings of passion and the way you kissed me on the train before we separated for three weeks until you, too, could go to New York. I think it was my birthday and you had given me a new suitcase, and I can see you also leaving that house with some of my baggage

43

on the way to the train in your car. We were never to return to that house.

On down Wildwood I walked thinking how you blotted out heartbreaks—when I thought I couldn't live for loss of love or not winning the wanted one. Passing the Alpine on Calhoun, I walked toward the bus that would be coming. There was Suttenfield where I lived for a semester before the apartment, again in a beautiful home. Also the gray stone church where we were married—and where I later heard a beloved student, Stan Possell, preach. On down a block on the left was the big house where I lived with Mrs. Hirons and Joan, Nada, and Vallerie at the time we were married. Just to the right was the Brown house where I had the lovely apartment with soft green walls—and oh, such happiness! There was a big balcony outside the front windows. It was more than I could afford, really, but you said you would pay part of the rent. We both wanted it so much, and we knew, we almost knew, that we would be married from there. But I squeezed out the money. Not having to buy every meal out, as before, meant a huge saving. And you brought food sometimes, and yes, you even cooked it. Your beef stew and your fried chicken were excellent. And we entertained Mom and Dad. And your mother. I was happy, but I took to crying when you left, and you cried there when your mother died.

What a shock to go into a restaurant for coffee and to have the doctor come and put his hand on your shoulder and tell you he had just left your home and your mother was gone. You had been with me within the hour, and Mamie had called for you at the apartment, so I knew first.

But there had been that "strange experience" in the hallway with the woman like your mother. I had put on a black floral robe when the doorbell rang. I thought it might be you returning. I talked to the woman at the foot of the stairs who said she was lost. It was not a dream—I remember quickly crawling back into bed with the robe on—I was frightened. As I lay there quivering, the phone rang, and Mamie told me the sad news.

That summer you kept house for your father. It was 1941, our first summer after graduating from Columbia, a rather bleak summer for both of us, no money, no summer jobs—just a sort of marking time. The next summer, in August, Grandpa died and I was out with my folks while you lived in the apartment and worked on the railroad. Also a rather bleak time.

Harold, from high school days, was drafted into the Army, and he was tormenting me to marry him. To please my folks and out of curiosity I saw him sometimes, but it wasn't anything. It simply showed me all the more that I loved you, what I perhaps needed after the frustration of our not being able to marry because of the money, where to live, war, your home situation, your railroad job, the possibility of my giving up my job after all that preparation, your possibility of coming to Fort Wayne, if single. We had nothing. We needed two jobs to buy a home. We were almost "pushing forty."

Mamie is in Colorado, Nellie said today. On a hunch, feeling Florence was home from the West, I called—"Yes, we got in half an hour ago." I just phoned about your marker and it will likely be ready Tuesday. Thus does love end, one after the other—seldom together.

I mentioned bleak summers two paragraphs back, but the teaching seasons were happy, always happy for us. We were part of the continuity of life when teaching, more than at any other time.

I wonder if I dare put on silver slippers and carry a silver purse with my green retirement dress for the AAUW tea tomorrow. Do you dare me?

September 26, 1971

Harry, Harry, I just rushed in after a song festival at Plymouth Church with Helen Burr. And the emptiness burst upon me till I thought I would burst. I missed you so! I know what my father meant about nights and Sundays and holidays being the worst. I watched Mr. Haley in church, but I wonder if there was the closeness that we and my folks had.

I thought I would not go to church this morning, but I went to the 11:00 service in a taxi and am so glad I did. Stopped at the chapel a moment for you, and got a cup of coffee, and listened to a good sermon on the sons of Noah and their covering him. Do we shield others and protect? I sat two or three seats back of Bill Hart and his mother, and I thought of his loss, too. These three men, and oh, ever so many women I know have stood loneliness after love—but me? You always said I would age with retiring if I wasn't careful. Oh, you counted on living—and not leaving

45

me doubly alone—without you, without my career. But you did say I was strong—and in other difficulties I know I found strength somewhere, but this—I don't know.

After church I went to Azar's for a brawny lad sandwich with onion and a cup of coffee. Home in a taxi. I pottered around, fixing up the house and reading the paper. Perhaps someone might come, but only memories of you came. I almost went to Gardener's for supper, but I walk the streets enough—so I fixed last night's rice and pork and had some tomato wedges with a peanut butter sandwich. The locust tree is so big. You really planted trees. I look out a lot at the yard and the roses and the hedge. I may have to move.

I worried about my arm and neck. Does the doctor know what he is doing? I worried about driving the car. I worried about cleaning the house. I worried about keeping myself outgoing and friendly. I worried about so many things—when I know I have so much not to worry about, really.

The truth is I would give anything to hear you squeak your chair again, or see you cuddle your coffee cup, or even to have you blow smoke in my face. Honey, the thought almost overpowered me, "Irene, I'd help you if I could." I know that is true, so true. Therefore, I accept the fact. And I rise to your desire, to be in tune with your awayness for as long as this dream lasts, and the reality is. In other words, I must really live while I am alive, and then whatever is, is. Courage and smiles and busyness and initiative. I said I would rise—have I summoned the qualities it takes to keep going? It is so hard to be in the company of women or be alone. And as for men—the truth is, even all through the years, there was never anyone your equal. You are laughing, but in pleased laughter.

October 5, 1971

Oh, honey, I've been having a real hard time—but that isn't the whole truth. I don't know how things happen—but maybe God sends help to blot out sorrow that is too deep. Last night my brother and Jon came. And he talks, tell how he feels, knows he will have to reach out since Gerry is gone and help himself. In this union of a double grief, in this sharing, there is a solace. Today Florence came, walked over—just to talk and share some of her time, I guess.

46

And Sunday Venetta came to our church to see me. And it was such luck I found her. I almost couldn't go because of the telephone repair man, but there was just time to call a taxi on impulse. After church we were with Grace at Ayres'. Then we went to Verna Adams' house. The European trips broadened friendships so. Bill Hart was at church, and Venetta had been with him at a banquet recently.

John Barden came on Saturday night—had wanted to take me to the Thirty Club, but my phone was out. Sewing Club was nice Friday. Margaret and Helen spent Tuesday with Florence and me, and today Margaret sent a letter and a booklet of cheer. Your sister Nellie spent Thursday with me, and I gave her some of your things and a bouquet of your roses. People are so good, and Grace said everyone remarked about how well I was "doing."

Well, not one has seen me shed a tear—you used to laugh and say I was ugly when I cried. I never dreamed the white rug by your bed would be a prayer rug and your bed a crying counter. But though it's bitter, bitter, without you, waves of sweetness merge and mingle until I can rise with courage because of all we have shared in our living together—such riches, such fun, such triumph over troubles, such working together.

The basement needs cleaning, no, it's the whole house. The yard needs mowing, and I have such troubles with the mower. There's so much arranging still. I called Frieda, Ruth's sister, tonight—she told me some things she did—it has been seven years for her.

Harry, your rose-colored stone with the two roses and both our names is up—and I think I like it. I got the best one I could get, I think. Florence and Ken took me out Tuesday evening, and we ate at the Pancake House afterward. I believe Nellie likes your stone. It just seems as if you ought to look it over with me.

I went to the hospital three days this week, and one day I walked all the way home. I did that once seven years ago when you were there. October's bright blue weather was with me all the way both times. The brown leaves rustled along with me. We crunched them on the way to our wedding that October of so many years ago.

Yesterday I found a gold cigarette lighter in the garage in an innocent looking box. When I tripped it, there was an instant light. Maybe I will give it to your sister, Nellie. I know not what tensions, what defiance, what enjoyment smoking afforded you, but somehow I always thought smoking might cancel out the effect of your medicine.

Anyway, please know, and I feel sure that you do, that I deeply, deeply loved you. When a person feels this and feels your love in the many, many expressions of it that are my memories, then there should be no time for crying. But I want your arms and I want to nestle my head on your shoulder where it always felt just right. I want a chance to say things to you and do things for you, but as Robert Frost says, "Nothing gold can stay."

Oh, yes, I remember the good and the bad—the way life really is—and we were comfortable together, I think—as comfortable as any two people can be. In the way that I have to go, I cannot imagine ever being that comfortable again.

It is ten of twelve, the death of the day, but a tomorrow will be.

October 10, 1971

Oh, Harry, I went to church with Helen, to Ayres' to eat, to her house for red dahlias to take to St. Joe Hospital, and then I came home in the afternoon to an ache I thought would kill me. But as the Bible tells me, "Blessed are they that mourn, for they shall be comforted." The telephone rang three times, and I was invited out twice, but as the old man said, "They asked me for mannerly's sake, and for mannerly's sake I refused."

It does seem though that when I think I can't live without you, help, or a sense of calmness, interfuses and I gain strength somehow. Do you have an influence? Or do I just somehow realize the riches you have given me and the blessedness of our years together? For all you have given me, how could I ache or cry? Did I give you enough joy? Enough peace, pride, love? Oh, marriage can be the most wonderful experience on earth! And never, never would I have exchanged you for any other. "Don't kid me," you say? No, never about that. "I love you too, Irene."

Well, in sixteen days is our twenty-seventh anniversary—and I, well, somehow I will get by, and then there is Thankgiving, and then there is Christmas, and then this year of the greatest loss and test of my life will end. There will be a New Year, and Valentine's Day. Your birthday, March 3rd. Spring Vacation in April—all of April for both of us—and Easter. Then in May, Decoration Day. And in June, I will be a whole year older, without you. The leaves will color and go. The snow will fall and blow.

48

Your tulips and roses will grow again.

Honey, Venetta had some pictures of the trip to Europe, some I hadn't seen, and I did look pretty in them. Was at Joe's party and at Ethel's house—two different days—I go a lot. But I was proud because you would be of me—just as I was always proud of your appearance.

I can still see my brother crying and hitting the table—his way out at the time Gerry was taken to the hospital. He wondered the last time he was here if he was cooking right for the boys. And he washes the clothes and cleans the house. And Florence was alone for so many years. And Dad for thirteen years. The happiest time is the family time, or is it the new family time?

Well, Harry, I do hope to stay sweet and sane, even though I sometimes feel reason could snap. I shall keep busier and let the warm undercurrent of the love we both knew buoy me up, and not let the loss pull me down. I shall look out more than in. I suppose there are other hurts worse than memory where sweet love has been, and has been taken by death, and such a quick, quiet, genteel leaving.

October 16, 1971

Oh, Harry, the world out the front window was so vivid this morning when I pulled the drapes. Von Patten's maple tree was agleam with the usual red leaves vying with the green and gold. And the patch of blue sky on beyond! A friendly street with homey houses, and yes, our lawn was mowed and neat again. Oh, honey, the morning ache is nothing like the evening ache, or the ache on coming home and expecting unconsciously the coming together that was always such a joy for me, and you too.

I took the 7:20 bus and met Venetta at the shrine for the Lebamoff breakfast and to hear Major Lindsey of New York. It was all very interesting. Your New Haven youth sang a group of songs. We talked to a Negro leader married to Central's Mary Clark. The mayor is so handsome, maybe the next President. He speaks well with such sudden charm.

Venetta and I went to Ted and Tom's South for Greek salads and garlic toast and coffee. Shared a grasshopper drink with her. Watched a ball game as we ate in congenial surroundings in the bar room. Then we went to Ayres' South where she bought a beige sweater and I bought a white scarf. Home, for a dozen Pepsis, I

49

let a young man from South Side demonstrate a sweeper outfit. Ours is still so new. You were so eager to buy it for me before the first trip to Europe.

Sherry had her appendix out instead of her "cancer" and will have to live with some side pain because abdominal fluids are not readily absorbed. Ken and Florence had wanted me to eat with them at noon.

All three closets are in order. Your living room one has many of your clothes yet. The car has gas Florence and I got yesterday, so I will have to drive next week. I paid the lawyer's bill of $2000 this week. I packed the wash and cleared out some things from the basement. Oh, Honey, I miss you so! Mr. N. got the lawnmower fixed for me.

I don't stay home very much. I can't settle down. I got a haircut and a permanent. I will have to keep pretty as possible for your sake, if you know what I mean. My eyeballs ached and were so grainy this week—I suppose I supress striving tears, perhaps sometimes unconsciously.

Had a delicious supper party in Monroeville on Thursday night with people you know, the Sidells. Venetta showed our European pictures. It was an A.A.U.W. section group. Such good chicken breasts with thick mushroom gravy, rice, green beans, etc.

I gave Florence a bouquet of your roses last night. The mums at the corner of the house are more beautiful than they ever were, such rosy-lavender slender petals, so many blooms. The marigolds are gay with yellow and bronze and maroon. I never knew when I married you how much you loved flowers. I will always remember what the minister said about your quiet, gentle ways and your love of the out-of-doors. I can see you slowly, gently, carefully setting rose stems into the ground for future bushes and blooms.

Florence said she would always remember the soft way you said "Irene." There is so much to remember, so many riches that can never be measured in money. Just remember, honey, that I thank you and appreciate with love as great as any woman ever had for any man. And I hope any hurt I ever gave you never nicked your feeling for me. You sounded so happy that last night from the kitchen, and in the study too. Oh, I know we must accept it as a God-given way to go. And I must be thankful you left as you did. And I must see it sanely and keep sane until I, too, leave this world where we loved.

I stood with Venetta in your beautiful chapel after we went to the library today. I saw you walking up the aisle to the altar with the offering, and also serving communion—a white carnation in your lapel. I sat by you and heard your voice in song. How handsome, how erect you were! And how sweet and pleasant! Am I not a lucky woman with such memories?

October 19, 1971

Oh, Honey, this had been a day! After breakfast and a bath, I knew I'd have to get out. The front window boasted two red roses on the bush alone, and the maple tree across the street was in a scarlet ball gown. The clear blue sky and the green grass will vie awhile with the gold and rust and scarlet of the leaves. The locust you planted is pure gold.

Oh, it took awhile for me to get ready to drive. But I had to do it—drive the beige and green car you liked so much. I like it too, but am more then a little fearful of driving. I went to the laundromat with the green spread and blanket and then sailed south to your Tillman Road on to the Hartzell Road and the cemetery. It was so beautiful at the entrance—the yellow and red trees along with the evergreens. It was almost heavenly around the curves to your and my marker. Somehow it didn't seem sad, and I wanted my brother to see it, so out to Hoagland I sailed again.

Lloyd drove his car in to see "our place at last," and we walked around noting his friends and our friends who have stopped walking. Then we went to the Chevrolet place where you bought the car and talked to two men. Lloyd showed me a car like Jon's new one. Now I know how and where to take the car if it needs something.

Came back at 1:00 and ate a bite of lunch. Then Florence came over—it's her birthday—so we drove out to Marilyn's—I drove. Took along some washing essentials of yours that I do not need, and also some pencils and other things. When we came back, I walked to the laundromat to get the spread and blanket, for exercise. As I was hopping along, I felt how proud you would be of me for driving, and for trying to be happy.

But when I settled to eat my supper, my neck hurt, my eyes hurt, and my head ached. Strain perhaps, but the strain of success, I hope. I rested awhile and thought of how good you must have felt after supper when I put the blanket over you and let you rest.

Hope, the European tour friend, called from Indianapolis and wanted Venetta and me to come this week end. I had written her about it, so it looks as if fun and adventure are in store. The mayor's wife's prayer breakfast is tomorrow, also the last driving class. Venetta's Hawaiian supper on Thursday, hair done on Friday. Venetta just called and we talked about the trip to Indianapolis.

Oh, honey, it's just a week from our twenty-seventh anniversary. Oh, to hold you close again! Our ecstasies more than balanced our sorrow and pain and trouble. And there were the smooth, merely happy times, like going down through Mississippi at Christmastime or eating many a good meal together. I'll never get over the "can't-wait-to-see-you" feeling I always had when separated from you, even for a short time. That, I think, and the touch of you are what I miss most. There were never any hands like yours—the quilted palms, so warm, sweet, reassuring.

I did call Mamie to ask her and Mike to come for supper, but she took a raincheck—talked a long time. Good night, Harry. Oh, to turn back the years, to be able to have a second chance, to live it all over again. It was so full of wonders. I picked a bouquet of roses for the table this evening. I can see your hands placing roses in vases, one after the other. I can see you giving roses as gifts. It is just one of the joys of our marriage.

October 22, 1971

Hi, Harry, this morning and again this evening I pulled the lovely blue floral kitchen curtains apart to stare at the dark red roses trying to say hello to me, a full one, a half one, and a bud. There were covered with shining rain beads. It rained all last night and all day, off and on.

I got my hair tinted and bought a brown purse and shoes to go with the new dress and jewelry purchased at Nobbson's Wednesday after driving class. I love brown and gold. Tomorrow Venetta and I drive to Indianapolis in her blue Skylark—will stay at Holiday Inn #3.

The prayer breakfast was fine—a beautiful singer who did "How Great Thou Art" and two others. A woman spoke on prayer—her son is married to Billy Graham's daughter. Truly, enough women with enough prayer might accomplish wonders for our country.

We sat near Ruth Fleck, Amelia Dare, and Florence Trader.

The Hawaiian banquet at Hall's party room across the bridge by the Clyde Theatre was wonderful with Venetta and Mary Ellen. I noticed the wives, three especially who nudged so close to their husbands' arms during the program, and the husbands seemed so pleased, so comfortable.

The last time we lay on the bed together I was so afraid of hurting your left arm. I do not want to pine away for lack of the touch of love. I must have been cuddled a lot when I was a baby living in my grandparents' home with parents, three young uncles, and a great grandmother who helped me get born. The sweet, clean appeal of you and your gentle ways made me happy, so very happy. No, I am not talking nonsense, it was ever thus.

Sometimes for moments I almost go wild with missing you, and am so frightened about facing life alone, but there comes from somewhere a sort of peace and courage and wisdom, and even a tiny measure of the old natural gaiety. If you have anything to do with it, or if my talking with God does, I hope it magnifies and magnifies. I thank whatever powers that be!

The little overnight case is here by me; I'll pack it in the morning. You always helped me so much on a trip—traveler's checks, mouth wash, hair spray, perfume. And did I have enough money? And always that good-by kiss. And unshed tears as I got on the way—and then that glorious rush of together again after the trip! It was always fun to send you cards and bring back something for you.

I ought to be adjusted; it is just a little short of five months. I can try harder, I suppose. But I believe I do better by talking it over with you than by just pushing my true feelings away. My brother said, "Losing parents is bad, but losing the one you have talked to about everything through the years is worse." It is difficult to not have that exchange of confidences, that loving communication—or those arguments! So I suppose, after a time, the realization that I am me, alone, and it is my life, and things are mine, will begin to dawn with a severe finality, but it all seems so selfish, so one-sided. Perhaps I can learn to "sing a solo" and be as lovely and brave as the dark-eyed lady at the prayer breakfast. I keep trying, God knows, but you would have me win. And with all the many forms of wealth you have given me, I will win. I will be happy, courageous, and useful, because you have loved me truly. And I will remember your pride in appearance, and that you had pride in mine. You said some lovely things for me to remember.

October 26, 1971

This, Harry, is the day, the wedding anniversary! When we were married on the twenty-sixth, we couldn't know that there would be only twenty-six years together.

I have just taken off my bra and girdle—I know now at 9:00 p.m. no one will come—so I am very comfortable. Florence and Ken walked over about 11:00 and I wanted to get dinner for them, a simple, quick one. It was so good to eat with people here. Then about 2:30, after they had gone, Mamie came until Mike could pick her up at 4:30. I was glad I was wearing my pink floral swirl and fixed up, and I was glad the house was in order.

I had to get out and walk at suppertime—ate at the CharKing and shopped at Maloley's. Then I swept up the locust leaves; the golden tree is now a black lace skeleton. I know you would have loved to do it and to winterize our flowers and the house, but I will get along. I will take care while you are away. Your work caps still crown the garage, the Smitley girls reminded me—like Peter Marshall's white shoes under the bed at the lake cottage.

The weekend with Venetta in Indianapolis and Brown and Green counties was good for both of us, Hope and Welcome and Phil were delightful. I felt a desperate ache as I walked with Venetta to our room. Always before, you and I stayed at Holiday Inns. And then I thought of her not ever having what you and I had—and I felt wickedly selfish. Right now, she is my closest friend, and I am glad you liked her so much.

The trees, the hills, the mist, the fog, all were right. All the feelings between us were right—getting to know Welcome better, the European chatter and pictures, the good food at various places and at the Kopper Kettle, the cider and popcorn, and the ice cream cones at Nashville all added to a charming bit of time.

A mobile home can be a new way of life, but our home, honey, I know you loved it. I showed off the four red roses that peek in at the kitchen window, pulled back the blue floral curtains for all who came to see. The marigolds are masses of blooms, and the mums too. The salmon-colored geraniums and the red salvia are pretty groupings.

A lot has happened, really since I got home at 2:00 yesterday. Unpacking, putting things in order, reading *The Source*, a book my brother gave me. I don't really miss teaching, as you thought I would. In fact, I only taught children one day after you left, though I finished the clerical work those two days, June 10th and 11th, when the children were forbidden to come back because of threatened trouble and demonstrations. Cards were mailed out, and I walked to the bus with what little I took home. Without you it would be no fun anyway—we had a real momentum going—minutes of mighty motion. Such a sudden stop was hard on the gears. But a little accomplishing each day will show results.

If I had my way, I'd try writing short stories. Why not? When I get the machinery of keeping house going, and when I shake off some of the ache, perhaps I can plunge into a story and finish it. A sense of shame just swept over me, because even though I do not have you close, I have so very, very much, and I know that I ought to be happy and busier and grateful. "Bless us, O Lord, as blessing thee, we accept these, they gifts."

Papa smiled and waved good-by to me, and you pressed and re-pressed my hand in your "going." I just looked up at the picture taken on my wedding day, the colored miniature. It had been in the bottom desk drawer for ages. Earlier, I took my Bible and read the anniversary cards that came at the end of our first year. I don't know if I have the others. In clearing out some of our clutter, I may come across them. I am not sure what we did last year, but this I remember—you always did something, a card, a gift, a check, a dinner, or sweet love of some sort. Your checkbook says you gave me twenty dollars last year, and for the twenty-fifth anniversary you gave me a lovely white gold watch. Always generous and sweet. Should one try to forget such happiness? Or will a natural healing take place better if one takes honest looks when one feels like it? Just so I do not get to feeling too sorry for myself. As with clearing out the clutter, I believe sweeping up the heart will help. Or am I dawdling over an emotional task? I know this—I liked being with you. I liked it so much I cannot quite get over so soon not living with you after twenty-six years and seven months of unity.

October 31, 1971

It is the last day, Harry, of October, an October that has been triumphantly beautiful, and one that I shall always remember. There are three beautiful red roses in a white vase here on the stand at my left. I just kissed one of them. Today, after church, Helen B. and I drove to Huntington for dinner—the trees are mostly golden and brown, some lacy black.

Last night I hit an "awful low" when the people from Indianapolis and Venetta left about 1:15. There had been a big party at Joe Lillich's, and I had talked to Gardener at the CharKing about his and my loss. His heartfelt sorrow came over the wires to me after I gave your name for the pies. Each of us so well understood the other. When I went to get the pies, John Bardon and I had a long talk in the sunshine—he had just eaten two hamburgers. I went in and got a cheeseburger and coffee. Florence later helped me get some other supplies and inspected the house. Oh, honey, after all the excitement was over—afternoon trick-or-treaters too—I just couldn't absorb the quietness here without you. I ought not complain—you have given me so much—but wave after wave of emotion rocked me so that for a little while I was a "sinker."

Then again in church (six hours sleep isn't enough) I wanted to live it over—to gather you up in my arms in the basement, to at least put something soft between your cheek and the cement, and to tell you that I loved you. That, instead of rushing to the phone for the doctor and the ambulance. And why, again I say it, why didn't I ride with you instead of following in the police car?

But I can really only be here and go forward and do what needs to be done as best I can. The yard was mowed Wednesday all at once. The man from Mark's Garden Center had to come over about the mower, but now it will work fine. The hedge, the roses need help, the windows need washing. The house, oh, Honey, the house is so still without you. And we fixed it together, and we enjoyed it when we saw the results. It was our first house, not our first home. A little each day I can do to it to keep it pretty, and me pretty, and the yard pretty.

Joe had a Pan-Am picture for each of us, and, Honey, I did look pretty in the front row in my striped raincoat and rainhat. Right away I wanted to show it to you. You know, on those tours, there were so many widows and unmarrieds in comparison to couples. Why should I grieve when I have so much company? Oh, Honey,

56

it was so wonderful to find you and to have you for so many years! Why should I wail? I had better "look up, and laugh, and love, and lift."

The first meeting of the Woman's Club, and the A.A.U.W. supper at our church were Thursday and Friday—a harpist at one, and a Pennsylvania woman senator at the other. The male harpist sang many touching songs. Went to one with Lucile and Margaret Wingate, and to the other with Venetta. I think I looked pretty at both, but how I wanted your O.K., which you so generously always gave me.

Five whole months are now gone without you; soon, no not soon, a half year will be lived without you, without the touch of you. I just kissed your red rose nearest me, now I am ready for November.

November 3, 1971

Darling, it is here—winter—and so chilling. I drove out to Lloyd's today and spent an hour after taking my clothes to the laundromat, and then having to return because I had forgotten to put them in the car. It was a pretty day, but I had on a heavy dress and a blue sweater. The car drives so smoothly, and I did get it into the garage alone.

Do you know what? Lloyd and Shirley say Gerry was smoking in secret in the basement—little caches of cigarettes and matches were found. I think I can understand, because there might be bottles in my basement if things seemed hopeless to me.

Yesterday was Election Day, and I went to the new City-County Building to check on the inheritance tax, but it was closed. Then being in the vicinity of the Rose Marie Hotel, I went in for the first time since my retirement dinner. Got a baked pork chop, fried potatoes, slaw, and guess what—I ordered a glass of port which they wouldn't serve me because it was Election Day. I had better "get with it."

I went to the library and got a book on *Learning To Live as a Widow*. It was after my eye treatment, the second one. Read all I wanted to last night in between election returns. Of course, lawyer Lebamoff is now the mayor, and I won all my Democratic votes but one, Schmidt—the first time in my life I ever voted straight Democratic.

Monday I checked poetry for Mr. Baldus. So much all the time

57

keeps me so busy. When I think, I can be very lonely. I fairly ran last year to catch the early bus home to you. And, oh, the good feeling when I saw you! These walls need to surround love and laughter and purposeful living! I do not like just being "me."

Honey, Mr. Whiteman is lying among the flowers at 3:00 tomorrow—a heart attack at sixty-nine. You and he lived in the same house at college in 1936, or was it the year before? I should like to go to Portland—even considered driving alone.

But I go with Ruth Fleck to Woman's Club at 10:00, and to St Francis College for supper with Venetta, then on to Helen Lee's house afterward. In between, Lucille wants some time for Helen Hartley. The next day is the Retired Teachers' Luncheon, and the funeral is at 1:30. So I won't be there—oh, what a lot of my life is bound up with Mr. Whiteman, my first beloved principal, who encouraged me so to go to Columbia and to be a high school teacher. He was the man I admired most for a time. Saturday I guess I am going to a church supper with Florence and Ken—out to Antioch.

I brought in the cactus plants and picked four roses from under the kitchen window. Frost is the prediction. I which you could see the beauty and fix the back yard roses. They need you. It is convention time, so you could do so much. My, how the holidays have been juggled! Ann Netterfield called for me to attend Teachers' Council, but I am going everywhere else.

The precious past—does anyone appreciate it while it is happening? Oh, I have just been dreaming of times when your dimples deepened and your eyes shone and your skin glowed. And there were times when you danced me around! I can hear your thank-you's and "I love you too, Irene."

November 4, 1971

It is convention time, and I am not a teacher or a wife, and how I ached as I came in just now, ready to rush to you, to tell you of the day. The anguish was almost unendurable for a few moments. And I know I must face reality, but it is easier if I am true to my feeling for you—then I seem to be able to handle myself. It is as if I must pour out old wine to refresh my pitcher with new—in time the old sweet wine may be lessened. Anyway I just have to talk things over with you.

Helen and Lucille were here today and we were happy until

Helen learned she had lost an earring, and then we went back to the Shrine after searching here. When we came back without it, Patty and Carrie hunted in the grass. They looked so nice, Helen and Lucille, but their men have gone through the pain of a heart attack too. We are all sixty, and that was once old to us.

The Women's Club with Ruth Fleck was fun. A man who wrote *Matador* spoke, and he has lived such an interesting life as a writer, musician, teacher, painter, bull fighter. The lunch was good and I was surrounded by interesting people with whom to talk. Also the dinner meeting at St. Francis tonight was grand. Sat with two of Walter's teachers and one from Smart. Venetta and I then went to the library that Jon likes so much—he told me about it on the way over. Finally she and I wound up at Helen Lee's penthouse party. The Lillichs were there, Mrs. Thompson, and Nancy Morgan, especially. It was fun for awhile, and then I became conscious of how much better home and your nearness would be, and I could hardly stay another minute. Maybe that is how you sometimes felt about people when I did not quite understand.

I have made quite a lot of headway in living alone, and I will not let you down. It will be six months when November is done. *New Haven Junior High Notes* had a tribute in memory of you and a student-written poem. You had so much pride. I hope it was not injured too often. I hope there was enough enjoyment and happiness and fulfillment. Anyway, please know that I want to extend your pride and as you told me, I do not want to do anything foolish.

Lowell Coats told me I was looking good tonight, and Joe Lillich said if I would be a group leader he would make the Asian trip less for me. I really keep moving, but I think that is the way you would have it.

It is 12:30 a.m. now, and I feel a sort of restfulness and peace—maybe I am getting sleepy, but I have a better feeling about your being away.

November 7, 1971

Hi, Harry, I have just come in from a spiritualist meeting, where I went with Jon in his new blue Chevy. And I made a chocolate nut sundae and a cup of coffee, and here I am—more ready to be enfolded by you than aught else. You know that! There was a beautiful German-speaking registered nurse who gave a sermon on prayer—the mountain-moving kind. Her blonde hair was piled high with long bangs in front. She was so charming and interesting. She said, "Oh, what a pretty color"—my rose dress, and that my aura was the same color, a lovely aura. By January or February I will begin to feel better. It's just as if I have been at the bottom of a pit. Then she concluded that there was a shadow over my belly and that I should watch it. I maintained that there was nothing wrong there—it struck me so funny. But maybe the "spirits" know—it could mean various things. Jon is to watch his pocketbook, not to spend what he will wish he hadn't later.

I suppose this was really a red letter day. I drove to Garrett on I-69 to Auburn because I missed the turn. Came home on 27 but turned too soon. However, I did get to Anthony Boulevard after an eastern excursion. I made it and finally got the car in the garage. Also I made my first drive to 8:00 church and even stopped at the post office, coming home on Harrison Street. Nellie called last night and asked me to dinner. Kevin is three, and there was a plastic train on his cake with three candles. Both other sisters and Veva were there. I just took one plate of the delicious ham and chicken dinner and had no dessert. Honey, it was hard, but I am glad I went, and I hope you and they are. Everybody was nice to me and nobody cried, but Mamie was on the verge. Part of the time it seemed as if you were there.

I have really no right to be sad, I suppose, but sometimes I fairly ache with anguish—like yesterday when the first snow-flakes danced while the roses and marigolds drooped. Sometimes it is so bad, I think I might even get an ulcer for masking my feelings. But telling you this way seems to be an outlet. It was so wonderful to be understood and to be cherished. See, I have had so much, and the memory is beautiful to maintain. The aura, the lovely aura, of having been loved! Shirley said, "Uncle Harry babied you. He sort of kept you in a glass cage."

Ken and Florence took me to a church supper at Antioch last night, and Roger's family surprised us. It was a glorious feeling to belong to the family group. Were with Marilyn's two youngest also, and spent time at her house while she and Ray worked at the church.

I found another bottle of Brisk yesterday just inside the half-basement opening—half used it was. Lighters, cigarettes, lighter fluid, mouthwash, room deodorants, all stashed away in hidden places. I never dreamed how badly you were "hooked." It's enough to make me take to whisky, beer, wine, as some of my ancestors did. I suppose some people try to be strong so hard that their weaknesses gain on them.

I wish I knew as much as you about how to control the basement odor, the furnace, the hot water heater, the roses, the lawn, the windows, the laundry, the car, the mower, and countless other details that make a house a home. I will keep struggling and trying to develop independence. My marriage, my profession—my status, my worth. I will wink back tears, I will step lively. I pray that because I have been your wife, I will reflect your pride and your sensitivity. Good morrow, kind sir. I loved you very much and was most at home in your sight and in your arms.

November 8, 1971

Darling, I have just said good-by to George Baldus and his Zenobia. We were checking over his poems and had a good time doing it. I really feel that I did some finishing of things today.

Mr. Thomas gave me your suit and a pair of pants he had tried to sell. Now they are here, and he says they are too good to give away—he suggested a price. Then after coming back on the bus with your clothes, I went to the lawyer's office with a check for the inheritance tax of Indiana. That clears everything. All done. And a quarter of a million dollars. Where do I go from here?

It's frosty and cold and clear. I should have driven somewhere today, I suppose. But I read more of *The Source* and sorted out some of the linen closet. I feel more confident because of seeing your sisters yesterday and getting some things finished today. Mrs. Baldus said I shouldn't think of my loss—think of other things, keep busy.

So, if I am not morose, I will think of you, and of me, sometimes. And I will do some things for you, and some in the way you would have me do, and I will smile and be useful and gradually I will get out of the slough of despondency I could sink into.

November 21, 1971

Oh, Harry, I have just come in out of the cold, wind, snow, and it is so comfortable in your warm house. I am, I think, almost happy. Ruth Fleck got me up at 9:00 for coffee at the church at

10:15. I quick called Helen Burr and got breakfast and a bath. I soon was ready to go in my orange dress and gold coat. I thought leaf bits were falling, so I put on a wind bonnet to keep my hair clean, but it was snow. After a sermon by the new minister on power-measuring people, Helen and I went to Ayres' for dinner and met Gretta, Gladys S., and Martha Gibson. Rushed home after shopping at Maloley's and made a five-way salad to take to Florence's Sunday school class party. Was with Vera Baumgartner. The older people this time did not seem as pathetic to me as in June. Oh, honey, it was a full day with lots of people—but I thought of you.

The reason I haven't written recently is because I was so depressed—the bitter cup of missing you was effervescing so violently that I did not know sometimes if I could take one more sip. It was the worst around November 11, the anniversary of the heart attack. Each year I would automatically count one more, one more you had made it, only this time it was impossible to count, impossible for you to live, impossible for me to live too. I asked, and I fumed, and I used the white prayer rug by your bed. I looked out the windows for you.

I cleaned the two back rooms thoroughly. I trimmed the roses. I drove to Hoagland. I went to two Women's Club meetings. I shopped for new clothes. I took Walter and Lucile to Ye Olde Inn. I went to another spiritualist meeting by taxi where I talked to your friend, Hawkins, the druggist, and his wife. I just kept so busy, trying to be normal, and knowing somehow I dared not fail. And that is the way it will be. I seem to get help or inspiration when I absolutely have to have it.

My European friend from Indianapolis sent me clippings she had found solace in when her husband was killed in an auto accident six years ago. Something, call it God's hand, call it your hovering spirit, helps me when I need help.

I know that I am emerging, a different person, perhaps a better one. I am more independent, more considerate, richer because of the deep love you awakened in me, but I want to be a better swimmer. No floating for me! And last week, even though trying hard to swim, I almost sank. God forbid! It's a new life I am going into, a new life, a new life—sometimes the record sticks; sometimes I may seem a crybaby, but I will swim through the unshed tears, eventually.

Florence just phoned me about the meeting at her church today. Venetta just talked to me about the horses from Vienna which we will see at the Coliseum, Wednesday. Joe Lillich wants me to be a leader of the Asian tour next summer. I have much to be thankful for.

Your sister Nellie invited me to Thanksgiving at the Rosses'. Helen Burr asked me. I may have it here alone this year, unless my family says something. Roger's family will be at Aunt Jean's. May see something of them. Nellie says Mamie is very much "not herself." Woodie may have to have an operation. Shirley's baby is due. I am thankful to have family and people and health and money. May I be wise in all ways, wiser than I have been able to be, perhaps, in the busier years ahead. May I really live the life I have.

I feel so sad sometimes about some of the hard things you had to endure, but from now on I am going to try to see you in your happy times—enjoying New Orleans at Christmas, caring for your roses, speaking at the banquet of the class you sponsored twenty-five years ago, in 1970, fashioning the winter holiday lights in the orange bush, changing your Studebakers, explaining school successes, watching me go over your Christmas cards from 1939 on, seeing you enjoy our meals together, priding yourself in fixing our home pretty. Oh, honey, there was joy, lots of it that I have overlooked because I loved you so deeply everything that hurt you also hurt me, and I was in a mood for hurting, I guess.

You lived with me a long time, you live with me and in me still, and please let's—I am talking to myself especially—please let's live joyously and purposefully in the radiance of God's will.

November 28, 1971

Honey, it has been six months since I put the blanket over you after supper, and you and I had our last sleep as two in this house. I seem to want to make anniversaries out of so many calendar dates. I got through Thanksgiving. When I turned to the Presbyterian prayer book for Thanksgiving, I found a line along the edge of the prayer carefully drawn in green ink. Perhaps you used it for a school program, or patriotic soul that you were, you may have simply liked the words:

"Most high and mighty Ruler of the universe, by whom our nation hath been established in freedom and preserved in union: In this feast of harvest we thank Thee for the fruits of the earth. We thank Thee also for Thy favor shown unto our fathers, and Thy faithfulness continued unto their children; for the rich land given us for an inheritance, and the great power entrusted to the people; for the fidelity of men set in authority, and the peace maintained by righteous laws; for protection from outward dangers, and deliverance from inward strife; for an honorable place among the nations, and the opportunity of increasing service to the world. Keep Thou the commonwealth beneath Thy care, and guide the State according to Thy will; and Thine shall be the glory and the praise and the thanksgiving, from generation to generation. Amen."

I chose not to go to the Rosses' or to Helen Burr's, just to stay here alone at noon, and perhaps have a visit with Roger's family in the late afternoon, but he couldn't make it to Jean's. However, Phil Nesbit called from the Hobby Ranch House and said have lunch with them before they went on to Detroit—Hope, her friend, and two grandchildren. I was ready for a bath, but I called a taxi for fifteen minutes later, and rush, rush. Venetta was there too. She and I had had a good supper at the CharKing the night before and then gone on to the Venetian horse show at the Coliseum. So I didn't fare too badly. Supper was a lone meal but I had the can of raspberry-cranberry salad you had thought I would enjoy sometime. Thank you.

Friday I got my hair done and bought a new splashy red-violet-gray-tan dress. It felt so good. Today I wore it to church.

Also last night when Margery Bell and Blanche Hutto told of their summer trip to Europe and the Holy Land, I felt so good in that dress. I wished you could see me when I was ready. Then tonight I wore it to Grace's house where Joe talked about the Asian tour. Honey, as you said, I am going to be a leader and get the trip cheaper. I may help Venetta with her expenses, but I know you would okay that.

It was hard to come into the still house just now, I miss you so. I have made myself comfortable in a nightie, and you would be in a tee shirt and pajama bottoms. We would have house slippers and be so much at ease. There was nothing like it—our being comfortable with each other.

Sometimes I forget, when the garbage is collected, to right the cans and they get water or snow in them, Then I have to upset them to drain and dry out, even if I take a flashlight and go out at night to see to it. It is hard to think of all the duties alone.

And your box of precious papers like your teaching licenses and our early tax and medical receipts and valuable letters and other keepsakes is not easy to straighten or to decide what to discard. I simply have to put it away for another time sometimes.

I went into the attic yesterday to look around. It was a rainy day. I opened the drawer where your Christmas cards to me since 1939 were. I wanted to see if last year's was there, and it was so beautiful, the one with the check for the 1971 European trip. I couldn't do much, just nosed around and came down with a pair of pillow slips I had never used—unwrapped they were.

I touch things you touched and I want to touch you. I feel the need for love, and then I am glad I am alive. I try to keep pretty and I try to keep brave and I try to be busy. There are quiet tears and quiet loneliness and quiet prayers. It is, all in all, pretty quiet. What others have accomplished in their losses, I can accomplish. I am not at all alone in that respect. But to have love and to lose it is a bitter lesson, Yet the rays of gladness for what was and what is can illuminate—what will be, will be, as the song says. I do not want to be sorry for myself; I just ache for you and for some of the things I said, and for some of the things we didn't get said. I just wanted a little more time.

Christmas season will not be easy, but I intend to work at it a little every day starting December 1. How thankful I should be for health and for a chance to do for you things you might want done! Everyone who celebrates this year will cross over before another hundred years. God's rhythms must have good reasons.

December 1, 1971

Honey, I just adjusted the drapes back of the gold chair, and a great, round golden moon winked at me from the east. That should spell joy, or at least happier thoughts. The last month of 1971 is here, and I am going to keep Christmas.

Today I cleaned the bedroom very thoroughly, and I put up Dad's white Christmas tree on the far end of my dresser. Every morning it will remind me to do other things that will add seasonal beauty to the house.

In my closet are two more beautiful dresses (Florence said so, too), and a new pair of navy shoes and a purse to match. My morale was ebbing yesterday, so at the Paris, on a hunch, I found both of them—a navy, red, and white, and a gold and blue. They fit in so well with my coats. And I have just checked—there are nine parties to attend.

I gave three of your suits to the Volunteers of America today. First, I slowly loved and examined each one, and I found tobacco hunks in one pocket, cigarette curls. The one we got in a hurry to go to Ed's father's funeral, and the other two you bought with pension-fund money just before you went back to school after the year out. I put two belts with each and the suits were nicely cleaned and pressed. The ties, the hankies, and two watches went along. Honey, you loved clothes—there are still others I must decide about. Oh, what fun it would be to dress up together and go out!

Florence brought the little book Mrs. Andrews wrote when Sonny was killed in Korea in 1951, a bridegroom of ten days when he left for training. I just read it all through this evening. A broken heart is anguish I know, a mother for a son, a wife for a husband, and all the other combinations. At times it is almost unbearable, and again a kind of peace pervades. We are not "all, all, alone, on a wide, wide sea of agony." The saints seem to take note of us, our angel loved ones, perhaps.

Your pension check came with mine today, and I said, "Thank you, Harry." As long as I live, I will gratefully do the same. I will remember your love which you passed on and on to me, the goodness of God through you. Could any man be more wonderful to a woman? And I can hear your, "I love you too, Irene." I hope I did and can still do enought to merit all I have received of heaven through your sweetness.

I bought stamps yesterday and a box of gold and blue cards, each with a huge white poinsettia. The envelopes are gold. I may address a few tonight. Remember, you always did that?

With the cleaning tonight, I mean today, I got myself into trouble. I still have a bath to take before I can crawl into the clean bed. Then there's the new *Good Housekeeping*. I read a spicy story last night about a seventy-five-year-old lady who joined a young family for Christmas dinner. It did me good to see how she made them sit up and notice she was more alive than they were. God help me to "keep kicking" as long as I may live.'

December 8, 1971

Darling, I just came in from the A.A.U.W. party at Ayres' Store. I left the porch light on, and it was so good to see the clean door I made today and your Christmas joy hanging on the thumbtack you put in when you bought the red and silver and green ornament. I turned on the light in Bob's Christmas tree in the window. So you see I am keeping up a front. When I put the Christmas cookies I bought into a container, I lifted a pink cactus bloom from Grandmother's plant and noted the three-tiered bell shape. I noted also that it bloomed last from Thanksgiving to Christmas in 1964, the time of your heart attack, and now again as if to cheer two of my heartbreaks. In one of the songs by the Elmhurst chorus tonight, after our fruit cup, two desserts and coffee, the words were something like this: "A house is not a home if there's no one to hold you tight, no one to kiss you goodnight."

Perhaps Venetta has felt that way too, or does, because I saw her cheeks and arms tremble. Her Mr. Meyer may have meant quite a lot to her when she said good-by to him and got home from Europe only in time to go to his funeral. Or there may have been someone once, or perhaps the ideal exists only in longing. How rich I have been with you—before I went tonight I looked through the white Kodak album to get some glimpses of you that were caught, in time.

There are six more Christmas parties; and there have been six, two Friday and two Saturday, and they were so delightful, especially the supper at Dr. Lillich's with eight of us trippers around the table eating Polynesian food and German chocolate cake and raspberry wine from somewhere. And the trip pictures were so beautiful. Venetta showed hers again. Dr. Lillich's mother is ideal, and even Mrs. Stout was more jewel-like than I had ever dreamed she could be.

I am giving Marilyn the red Christmas tablecloth from the "prom days" that I had thought to use this year, finally. It doesn't go with my browns and blues, but it may blend with her greens. I must keep Christmas, somehow. Daddy, even when he was eighty-six, before the eventful March, put up his porch lights with the big star, and there were candles in all the windows, and there was a twinkling snowman on the buffet. He had a big bouquet of poinsettias, a little white tree on the dining room table, a manger scene on the TV. There was usually a check for the three of us, bills in an envelope, or sometimes a gift like the crystal beads and earrings for his daughters and Gerry. Thirteen years without our mother, and yet he always kept Christmas, and he kept cheer the year around.

A nice man came to the door yesterday and sold me a half-bushel of delicious apples. I put them in the attic to keep cool because my ice box is full of grapefruit, and I have a box of oranges ordered. Oh dear, I shall have to have fruit salad instead of fruit-cake this year. Perhaps I can manage to have some people in, but you always helped me so much when we agreed to have com-pany—back when you felt like entertaining. Mrs. Martin and Mrs. Sidell from Monroeville said their husbands didn't care for social life.

It has been raining for a long while. There was water in the garage and it did not come from that crack. The roof and the side walls did not seem to be leaking anywhere. I think it splashed in from under the door because the back of the car was dotted with droplets. The Northside plumber came about the sewer gas, and I called the insurance man about the small broken window-pane up front. The Indiana tax form came today. Last night I hemmed the top of the peach blanket, and the bottom of it, the one that the teachers of Garrett gave us when we were married. The satin binding was worn, but the blanket seems as good as new. Must have it washed.

A phone call came from Indiana Technical College for me to teach at Bluffton from 6:30 to 8:00—a salary and ten cents a mile. At first it was tempting—it made me feel important and needed—but I am not that good a driver and I would not feel safe at night on wintry roads even if the class just met on Thursdays. I wonder who referred me to them for this English position.

My closet is full of pretty clothes I wish you could see. And there are matchmakers who are busy—but there never was or never will be anyone who can take your place. Mrs. Lillich said it had been seven years for her and her wedding ring was for keeps. I wear yours everywhere. I always loved it so.

There is so much I want to tell you—things that would be important to just the two of us. But I think I will go and get a big apple, and then I may watch the eleven o'clock news. Hold tight! Goodnight!

December 12, 1971

Hi, Harry, it is six days to Christmas, and it is snowing. I have just watched *Bonanza*, as we so often did, and once in a while a tear oozed out, but I can't say I've been too unhappy today. I have no right to say that, and you wouldn't want me to be unhappy. Besides, "You are ugly when you cry."

I put on the red coat you gave me over a green dress and went to church with Helen B. The minister talked about "fears." I sat on the right side of the church to break my custom. But before going into the sanctuary, I stepped into the chapel alone and put my hand on the back of the pew where you liked to sit, and I drank in the beauty of the window and the white pointsettias on each side. Then I saw you ushering with the white carnation in your lapel. And I saw you walking up front with the offering, you and handsome Mr. Wharton. I listened to you sing, and I felt your warmth and vibrant presence in the pew with me. It was a glorious Christmas gift—those memories!

Helen and I had a delicious dinner at Ayres' and then we went walking about town in the thirty degrees with wind. To her house and to Maloley's to shop. The "holiday bisque" ice cream was so good for supper. I had three servings with my weiner sandwich.

Mamie called to thank me for the plaque—Minnie and Nellie put theirs on the wall right away. I thought you would like them better than boxes of candy. The plaques were Helen Steiner Rice poems with roses and gold and butterflies, at least Mamies's had butterflies. Mamie is going to Florida for three months, but will come here first. Minnie is going to Shirley's with Danny and Woodice. Mamie will be at Nellie's on Christmas Day, and I can be too.

Shirley's baby is named Laura Lee, born December 4. She sent the most beautiful picture of the other three children. Oh, I wish you could see it!

I wrote to Donald Gentry in Colorado about your being away. The Christmas cards are almost done. I was going to ask Scott to put one from me on the teacher's bulletin board as you always did, but Lucile said your school was on vacation starting last Friday. Now, that is a surprise! You and I might have had two weeks together. Well, there are candles, three small Christmas trees, poinsettias, holly, Nellie's Santa-something in every room to keep Christmas. It will be as gay as I can make it in the time I am at home.

Monday I went to the Retired Teachers' tea and had a good time, even if some of the women didn't have the hooks fastened above their dress zippers, which opened with movement, and some of the men leaned closer to hear you, and there were canes and arched backs and funny walks. The sparkle was out of some eyes, and shaky hands held the refreshments. That, Honey, is not for you. Marvoline asked Lucile and me to lunch at Jonelli's for Tuesday this week.

Wednesday I played bridge at Florence's—eight women. Florence's house is a maze of Christmas intricacies, charming in a way.

Thursday and Friday I took your clothes to 3710 S. Calhoun for sale and to the Good Will. The closet will soon be cleared as it has to be. You had two nice closets here, and I had two. What will I do with four?

I am spending Christmas Eve with Lucile and Walter, the Plumanns girls, and Marcia and Terry. We are going to Midnight Mass and to Lucile's for breakfast afterward. They pick me up at 11:00. Marilyn is having me to dinner December 26 with sixteen people, twenty-three if Roger gets to come home. Between the two affairs, I think I might be happier here on Christmas Day.

Harry, I did a fool thing this week. You know how you delighted in choosing my card, and how I delighted in receiving them. Well, I found a beauty of a "wife card," roses in a snow white sleigh and a lovely verse about sharing, and scheming, and planning, and living, and loving. I could not resist this once—I had to buy it and I will sign your name and the date and put it under the white tree in your room. Also I bought a booklet called *Anniversary Reflections*, and it will be from you—a lovely collection of verse and sayings about married love. Do you remember the first Christmas in the apartment when you were ill and you cried because you couldn't get out to get me a card, and I walked through the deep snow to the drugstore to search for one you would like? And there was one year when you were working on the railroad on weekends and I got worried about my card, so I got it ahead, just to make sure, and you were glad I got one I liked. I will get all my Christmas cards from the attic and enjoy each one from you—and I will be happy. Honey, it is time for Dick Florea and the news.

December 22, 1971

Darling, it is almost Christmas. Yesterday Marvoline and Lucile and I lunched at Jonelli's. Before we went our separate ways afterward, we stood and talked a bit of you and Ed. After six years, the sadness showed in Marvoline's eyes and her mouth trembled as she talked about how difficult it is to be alone at times, and especially it is not easy to go to church, Perhaps it is because Ed's funeral was in the church.

In the evening I went with Florence and Ken to their Sunday school class party. Florence wore her wedding dress and looked all silvery. The turkey-ham supper was delicious with all the carry-ins. I took a coconut cream pie from Gardner's. After the Christmas film and the carols, Santa came. Each lady had to sit on his knee before she got a gift. I thought I couldn't—it seemed so silly. My gift was four nice juice glasses—I had taken pansy note paper.

And, honey, for the first time I dreamed about you, so warm, so sweet, so furious as you held me tight in bed—but alas, my mother was in the bed down the way and every once in a while she raised her head to look our way—so I just woke up and you were a fade-away. If I could really hold you, if I could really talk to you, I think we could be so happy. I am trying hard to be sensible.

I cleared up the desk papers and sent in the insurance bills to Banker's Life. I put things away. I took mail to the box at noon and again at 4:30, so I ate both meals at Gardner's. It was sunny and bright and the grass was very green, but it was in the thirties, cold.

Helen Burr just called to say Catherine Jackson had died today. I wonder how many years we taught next-door together. So many sobering thoughts come as I think of the many close ones who have gone on.

I go to the beauty parlor tomorrow at 3:00. Perhaps I can give the floors a Christmas cleaning and change the bed if I get to bed decently—on time. This living without routine is not really for me. Last night I sat up till 1:00—read some in David Reuben, the chapter on abortion. I don't think I like being old and rich and wise. But, of course, I will make merry and try to catch the glow of Christmas.

71

January 1, 1972

All day, darling, it has seemed Sunday. I have been inside except for a trip to the garbage can. The temperature is about forty degrees, the grass is green, the air is snow-hinted, the clouds are gathering, but there was quite a bit of sunshine during the day.

At midnight I opened the door and let the New Year brush my face after listening to Guy Lombardo at the Waldorf Astoria and seeing the Times Square crowds. I had been with Venetta to her church's supper from 6:30 to 8:30. She didn't want me to eat alone. After I came home she went to the hospital to walk her mother who has had an eye operation. Then she went back to her church for the rest of family night and then to a small party at Dorothy's—Dorothy has also had eye surgery in Indianapolis. People have troubles.

I had a big day yesterday. In the morning I took a big bunch of your clothes and your umbrella to St. Vincent's Store on Calhoun. Then I walked to the Blue Print for a red desk blotter and to Ayres' for gold candles. Met Lucile and Walter and they didn't care for the upstairs menu either, so we all ate at the counter downstairs. Walter got a new suit, Lucile a new formal, and they go to the Lebamoff ball tomorrow night. Came home with them. Cleaned the house, took a bath, washed my clothes.

Oh, honey, the old year is gone! I was not too unhappy today because I don't want to be—neither do you want me to be. But there are twinges of anguish sometimes, as when I gave away your clothes, found tobacco crumbs in the pockets, sent your bankbook to Defiance, or thought about other new years. Oh, it happens every day sometime, sometimes. I suppose it always will. I loved you so.

The Rose Parade in Pasadena was almost in line when I ate breakfast at 10:00, but I had time to get a bath and ready for possible company before I sat down at 11:30, seemingly with you in your big chair, until about 1:45, when the parade was over.

There was half of a ham that you bought a year ago at this time roasting in the oven. I put in some potatoes to bake, and I made a pot of coffee. Ate around three with a twinge of anguish, but I know I must not form that type of habit. Enjoyed some of the fruit salad that was left from what I took to the church. Yes, I lighted the candle Helen gave me for Christmas.

72

And the tree in the window is now burning as the porch light is shining on your door decoration. I must write you a bit about Christmas tomorrow.

January 3, 1972

Oh, Harry, I feel so full of wanting to tell you things and of wanting to listen to you. A taxi almost got me as I crossed Clinton on foot—it was in the last lane as I was going east to Warsaw and the light changed as I got to the front of the car. It is too scary to rethink.

Your name and the date were in the church bulletin yesterday to be remembered at the Lord's table, and the new minister read your beautiful name correctly. A lady behind me was softly crying—I expect her husband's name may have been on the list too. And then the sermon was about communication and bridging the gap (I Peter 5). He talked about touch and what it can mean—among other things. Your touch to me was always heaven, you were so warm and clean and sweet. No one else ever felt like that to me, and in 1939 I was mid-thirty and had lived mainly in a man's world.

Honey, I just drank my good cup of coffee. And as I was ready to sip it, Mr. Baldus came and brought me a book of his poetry with a nice appreciation written above his autograph. The book is nicely illustrated with drawings of his own. The telephone has rung three times: Dorothy Ridgway invited me to a luncheon next Wednesday; Lucile talked about the Lebamoff inaugural and the ball, and she invited me to play bridge this Wednesday at Mabel Ball's; Florence and I will go to Hoagland tomorrow morning to see Lloyd. I am not really much alone, but so very alone in the short moments of anguish I cannot at times suppress.

I went to all the banks today for interest entries. And I took the last of your things, I think, to St. Vincent's Store. On a hunch, I took one of your razors to Remington's and they gave me five dollars for it and told me to bring in the bottles of shaving cleaner. I had sauerkraut and sausage at Ayres' and then went out to the American Federal where I almost got hit by the taxi.

At home I found the checks, four of them, over thirteen-hundred dollars. The money is good, of course; but the life with you as we worked and saved and loved and used what we wanted was better. And the roses that seemed to symbolic of our life kept spreading their beauty and their frangrance—far, far better than gold or silver. You on your knees with the roots, and then standing proudly before me, presenting the blooms!

The tulips on the south side of the house are coming up. I am afraid their noses will get cold and covered with snow eventually. Surely there will be deep snow to be shoveled. I caressed the curves of your nearly new boots as I packed them today. My new shoe boots will have to move the snow this year.

Honey, I promised to write about Christmas. Well, on Christmas Eve, Lucile came for me and we went to her house for Walter. Marcia and Terry brought Leona and Bernie, and Terry's best man and his Maytime wife met us at St. Peter's where a year ago we were at Marcia's wedding. The church was decorated beautifully, and it brought to my mind the various churches and cathedrals in Europe. There was a black minister, too, and several black people in the audience. Walter and Lucile were married there in June before we were married in October—was it just last year?

After the service, we all went back to Lucile's and Walter served eggnog with rum. Then there was breakfast: fruit cup, sausages and scrambled eggs, fancy rolls, floating island for dessert, homemade cookies, and coffee. We talked and laughed and then entered a frosty, white world—no snow, just frost—and I entered the house with the morning paper at 3:30. At 4:00 I settled for bed until 1:00 p.m.

It was Christmas Day, a day I chose to stay at home though Nellie had invited me for a 4:00 dinner. I ate lightly when I got up, and then, after seeing that the house was in order and that I was pretty, I had my Christmas. There was a candle from Helen, the candle from Elaine in Decatur, the four fruit glasses from St. Luke's, and a Christmas sugar bowl and a cream pitcher from Florence. Marilyn had given me a poinsettia. Then there was the booklet about marriage that "you gave me" because I couldn't resist buying it at Howard's.

After the unwrapping of gifts, there was the ceremony we always had—the re-looking at the cards you had sent me from 1939 on. I read every one and studied the pictures as memories caressed me. It was not an unhappy thing, rather a quiet, joyous, almost two-some thing. And finally I came to the 1970 ones, for there were two that year, one with a fifty-dollar bill with which I bought a green dress and silver slippers to retire in, and one with a 350-dollar check labeled "for the 1971 European trip." The cards were so different, one delicate in white and rose-red, and the other heavy and encrusted with gold and red-red. Then, last of all was the 1971 card I bought from "from you to me." I won't do it again, I promise. But it had a lovely white sleigh filled with pink roses. Roses in the snow, you know—the end.

This must have been the evening of the *Lawrence Welk Show* and the *Andy Williams Show*. Anyway, I did have a delightful television show sometime in this Christmas era. Also a pork chop supper, a really good alone meal.

Then on Sunday, the next day, I went with Ken and Florence to Marilyn's for a family Christmas. Took pink and green bread and the marshmallow-coconut salad and deviled eggs. Aunt Jean was there with Mr. Raber, Roger and his family, and Mike and Val. There were nineteen altogether, and it was wonderful. I had given Marilyn the red cloth, and she used it for a runner over a white cloth. There were green candles and pine and other decorations on the table, and a big tree in the living room. Everyone was very happy, and the food was out of this world! Twelve of us were at the table upstairs, and the seven little ones had a pretty table in the basement. Jean and Florence and Val and I cleaned up afterward—we let Marilyn and Margaret visit by the tree. Home late—paper plates and help-yourself for supper.

I just noticed that I am resting this tablet on an orange book, *Live Alone and Like It*, which I have read today. It was purchased in 1939 before I met you. She says you have to picture yourself a gay and independent person and have spunk enough to get the picture across to others. I notice also that I have the title upside down on my lap.

Well, all through the Christmas season, the little ceramic tree lighted the window, the porch light shone on your door decoration, the candles the Danish family gave me glowed, as did Helen's candle. Every room still has something of Christmas. And that I must change soon. It is a new year, and after that brush with the taxi, I feel a strong urge for survival.

January 6, 1972

Oh, honey, winter has settled in, and I am fit to be tied. So I just sat down to let you listen, which you always did so well. Your tax withholding slip came today and it wasn't right. The annuity portion for tax exclusion wasn't listed, and the Dec. 25, 1970 check must have been added in wrongly. I called New Haven, and later Marcia. I did a lot of figuring and hunted for a paper I finally found after biting my nails through. And to think I used to keep school as well as keep house, but then there was always our going to school together and our supper after it was over, and you could look up and see me and I could look up and see you, and if not, each knew where the other would be.

I waded through the snow tonight to fix the garbage can—today was collector's day; and I took the basement brush last night and brushed the walks after a fashion. And I remembered my key, not to lock myself out in the cold.

Sunday I got worried about a gasoline smell in the basement and had a man out to check the furnace, and he found some leaks. Gasoline was really in the sewer drain—someone must have poured some in somewhere. He took a petrified bird out of the chimney door, and he checked the water heater. I thought it was maybe about to blow up—the collar is cracked. He drained some water out and said to order a new collar, but there is no danger. You always took such good care of me when I got a cold or worse. I guess I am just worse now, but I am not going to talk myself into something even worse.

Oh, I keep trotting. Tuesday Florence and I drove over ice to see Marilyn and Lloyd. He knows what I know and had been down to unload on Marilyn. In the afternoon I could hardly bear the blizzard, but I listened to *Days of Our Lives* and *The Doctors* on TV. And I cooked those two little chickens in the Dutch oven my father gave me. I can see the little old man carrying it ever so carefully, all dusty, into the living room at home to give it to me. Bless him! He, too, knew matelessness as did my sister, now my brother and I. Well, the chicken and broth on brown bread made a good supper with the potato salad I didn't know I had in the ice box. Food is a sedative, with candlelight. And the blizzard blasted outside.

I played bridge yesterday with Lucille at Mable Ball's and today at the Women's Club. There was a good luncheon and a good program by a writer's agent, Max Siegel, of Chicago. He gave us so much to think about, mentioned so many authors I've heard of or read. Am interested in a book called *Grief* which will be out in April, I believe. It has only sixty pages. I should buckle down and write instead of trotting. Sewing Club, tomorrow night; Dr. Lillich's, Saturday at 7:30.

Oh, honey, I love the shoe boots for snow. Last night Walter and Lucile took me to the Bonanza to have supper with them. You can always count on some friends. Venetta just called; we are going to sew at Ethel's.

Honey, I do keep pretty busy socially, and I see plenty of housework to do, but I miss routine and purpose. I am not at all sure I appreciate this women's world I am living in. I miss men and young people! My grandfather, my father, my uncles, my brother, my first nephew, my boys at school, and the men teachers were always stimulating. When I saw Porky Holt on TV tonight and remembered him in fifth grade, it was an undiluted joy. I relate easier to males, young or old. Do you understand that? Or do you think I am bragging? Are you as opposite as I am? Is that the normal thing?

You know, you told me, "I think when you are dead, Irene, you are dead. That's all." You said it slowly, thoughtfully. I wish you could tell me how it is. Then "heaven" is here, I mean, it was. I do not want to get my mind tangled more, not right now. I just want to come out of this and do a few things as I think you would want me to. Perhaps as I so order my life and so sense your pleased presence more, I can gain strength to say farewell until we meet beneath the rose-colored stone, and you take my hand and show me unceasing wonders and joys, greater even that those that follow wedding words and being carried over the threshold of the earthly home.

January 10, 1972

Harry, I am really not with it—if you know what I mean. We talked about how one of us could go at any time, but that talking didn't begin to instill how it could actually be. I haven't had a bath since Friday night before getting ready for sewing club at Ossian, and this is Monday night—never less than one a day was the old way. The house is a "boar's nest." And I start to do something about it, then get feeble.

However, I did wash, repaper, and straighten the top cupboards Saturday and Sunday. Because I was short on paper, I called a taxi at 10:30 and went to church bathless to hear a sermon on

77

negativism from I Samuel 14, I think, and then I went to Ayres' for the paper. Ate at Azar's and taxied home. The streets were clear of snow and wet. Took my umbrella. The grass looks as if it needs a mowing.

The annuity fund was missing on the withholding statement, and the new one was wrong, so I called New Haven and the Lincoln Life before I understood it, or before Mr. Bell knew why it was as it was. So I spent some time mulling over the taxes and your checks. How glad I will be to get the taxes settled and the house in order. Maybe there is hope for me.

Any Woman Can by Reuben came today, and I read some of it—about widows and unmarrieds. His main idea is for a widow to marry a man younger than she is, and to marry one of her husband's friends or relatives. I thought over several, but I know I just couldn't get close to any of them. This house is so quiet. Everything stays in the heap I put it. Since all the dishes and glassware are newly washed, I should clean the silver and have a party.

Honey, yesterday, when I put the Christmas things in the attic, I looked in your trunk and saw a big brown envelope with pleated sides. It had some pictures, your mother's purse, your Manchester diploma, and your letters and cards to your parents in 1939 from New York. There were thirty-eight of them, one almost every day. You were rooming with Walter and you seemed to like him, and you talked of Ed and Rowe. I found one where you told about our first date—the only one until teacher's convention time in October. I was dating George. Those letters truly show how good and sensitive you were. Sometime I want to read all of them more carefully. I was so restless yesterday.

I took all the four-leaf clovers and other precious things out of the Bible I bought with my first teaching money. The cover blackened my hands and clothes, and it was best to burn it.

I have been cross-stitching the tablecloth some every day because sewing relaxes me. Venetta and I went to Ossian together, and we stayed after the other four left. I really enjoyed the whole evening, especially the eats Ethel always has—hot chicken sandwiches this time.

I suppose I could retire from retiring on a moment's notice, if there could be any stepping back in time. I sat by a young man in church who was so fastidious and read so precisely and sang

78

so well, as did you. In your trunk I found a printed rating sheet of yours, you were so honest. You especially rated your appearance tops and also your ability to speak creditably before a group. You had pride, and I will not let you down, but I cannot take a bath at 10:15.

Little by little, ache by ache, and effort by effort, I guess I will be all right. Only you know how I really feel, because you were my truest friend. So far, I have been able to "act a part" around others. With you I could always be myself, and it was the other way too. We loved and trusted each other, even with a few differences of opinion on a few occasions.

If I could have had this year to make life a heaven on earth for you, then I might not feel so bad about retiring alone, or vice versa. But I can make it a heaven on earth for your memory. I can honor your pride, your love of order and cleanliness, your wishes for me and others, your ambition to be busy and interested in the world. I can be of good cheer, I think.

January 11, 1972

Honey, I did get a bath about 4:00, and it was wonderful. All clean clothes, fixed my hair, used cologne.

And I did work on the kitchen some more. Washed the lower south cupboard inside and the broom closet and the north wall. Put up my calendar from Denmark above the white chair where Venetta told me to put it. Eventually the kitchen will be clean. A newspaper in the top of the broom closet said July, 1969, so I think that may be the last time we cleaned house together. I did the kitchen and bath, and saved the ceilings for you. Also I got the step ladder out and cleaned the front window.

I still had time for some TV—red-headed Irish children in the midst of Belfast turmoil, such charming kids, so many of them. There was time for finishing the big cross stitch design on my tablecloth. Now I will put it away until sewing club; there are still two big designs and one small corner one. And, of course, there was some time for reading Reuben.

Naturally I thought a lot about us, but it wasn't too sad. Thoughts just well up in me, and perhaps it's best to be free with them rather than stifle them. You were the best thing that ever happened to me, and I loved you dearly. When the yellow room was pale green and we had your bed from home amd my old

79

dresser and chest, it was a haven of delight. Finally we switched the bedroom and the study. Mr. N. came to help us move things, and the bookcase became a real problem. Then came the new bedroom suite, but we were used to the old familiar first. I wonder if most married people are together the way we were. Our jobs, our Manchester and Columbia backgrounds, our spontaneous feelings, our absolute trust and reliance when in need, in trouble or in illness. It is a bitter blow to be without you, but no one shall know just how bitter. That's the way I have always been with the sadness in my life. They say God never shuts one door without opening another, and that is the way it has been with all my heartbreak. In due time, all has had meaning.

January will go, and then in just four months it will be a year. And your tulips and roses and the orange blossom bush by the door will gladden all who look upon it. And I will look and partake of your love, your strength, your gentleness, your goodness. I think you were happy in your school, in your home, in your yard, and in your church.

January 12, 1972

Darling, a Central girl, dark Jacolyn Bell, just called to talk and tell me about school this year at Northrup. Among other things, my voice sounded just as peppy, and I, at school, moved around lively, and younger than I must be. I told her you always said that. Just when I needed something to live by, she made me feel so much better by stimulating a desire to be anything but resigned or retired.

And, honey, your sister, Minnie, sent me some pearl and topaz beads she had made. I may wear them with my brown dress to the Woman's Club luncheon tomorrow. Two happinesses today. Still there was another.

There were six for luncheon at Dorothy Ridgway's—four maiden ladies, a divorced one, and widowed me. There was a pretty green table with delicious food, a fire in the fireplace, and good talk. Affairs like that are lovely, but I wanted to come home to you afterward so much that it hurt.

I have thought at different times today about those two last suits you bought, especially the one with the brown stripes that I gave to St. Vincent's. Remember how you would bring home samples from the tailor and we would feel them and look at them in different ways and at different distances. It was always a ceremony that we delighted in, and finally we would choose maybe three and then narrow the choice down to the needed one or two suits. And those lovely colored shirts of the last year. All gone.

I am still reading Reuben's *Any Woman Can*, and so much of his advice applies to our back-when days of finding each other and learning to love. Today is my brother's wedding anniversary, forty-three years, only last year he still had Gerry, but in the hospital. I called Florence and she remembered. Jacolyn Bell, tonight reminded me how well I did on the day I came back to school after your funeral. And she is going on to Purdue, and if she marries, I can come to her wedding.

Reuben says any woman who spends a big part of her time away from the attentions of men gradually begins to lose confidence in herself as a woman. Vague feelings of doubt and inferiority creep into her life slowly, almost imperceptibly, the glow of optimism and the warmth that are the very essence of feminine attractiveness begin to fade . . . So I guess I see why I had a lively step and a ring in my voice and a younger-than-I-am look. "Thank you, thank you," you say.

January 26, 1972

Harry, this morning I got a call from Marguerite C.—she had just come home from a before Christmas visit to a ranch near Billings, Montana. She and her brother drove and saw some mighty drifts while there. Her brother lives in a built-on addition to her house. She says he is away traveling quite a bit and that being alone is just awful. Her Howard and you left us the same time almost, he in August, you last May. And, of course, I could echo her feelings. Sometimes when I am eating, a spasm of loneliness locks my throat and I can't swallow for a minute. Or it will suddenly redden my eyes. I miss you so. I love you so much.

Nellie called to have me fix her taxes. Minnie called to talk—Woodie has to have a prostrate operation. Mamie is in Florida, but she has had a bad cold. Your three sisters, but you are with your parents, the first to run "home." Darling, your letters, have I mentioned reading them? The thirty-eight you wrote to your parents from New York in 1939, the year you had your first date with me. Anyway, I have reread many of them, and they show your true character, your honor for your parents, your goodness, your real self. How glad I am to have them!

Other things in your trunk I will do away with, as I will do with many of my things. It is better than for others to cast it out. Your high school sweater, your mother's shoes and purse, your father's cap and billfold. It hurts that we can't do it together, but I shall be careful of your treasures.

Florence and Ken came to help me about a "man who it seemed I should not let in the house." I got them a good dinner and he fixed both screen doors, put a new lock on the back one. It means so much for me to have them near, six blocks away. The insurance man came today, but he was legitimate, about my Banker's Life policy.

I wrote checks for the car insurance and the house insurance. I must be driving again since there is not snow and ice. I walked to the laundromat with the laundry and grocery shopped on the way back. It was sixteen degrees, but I enjoyed the crispness, enjoying it again when I went back for the laundry in three hours after watching TV for an hour: *Days of Our Lives* and *The Doctors*.

Ruth Fleck called and we ate supper at 6:00 at the McKinnie Tap in a cozy corner. Left at 8:00, full of spaghetti, garlic toast, salad, and coffee.

Honey, I know you are glad there are so many friends. Lucile is taking me to the Woman's Club tomorrow. And there are my people, and your people too. This is all very wonderful. But the endearment of arms about you and a nestling shoulder and the familiar, yet ever new, "I love you" is only a remembered thing. And the sweet wildness of moments of marriage, was that a dream thing?

The 11:00 news calls, so I get up and go.

February 3, 1972

Oh, Harry, it is a night! The Reed Street sign trembles in the wind, and the locust black lace branches lost and relost their patterns. Snow swirls danced about and two children fell on the ice, the one with a sack of groceries.

After coming home with packages for sewing club tomorrow night, I felt I had to go to the grocery for cream and coffee and cookies. Otherwise I could not sleep. There is a hair appointment tomorrow at 10:15. But it was treacherous underfoot and snow and ice impeded. It is so good to have everything—you would have

82

helped, you always helped so much when I entertained.

I bought three delicious-looking delmonico steaks and fixed one for supper. Pink grapefruit and melba toast—and best of all, I made a pot of coffee and drank it all. Of course that called for the broken "heart" cookies, and one called for another. I ate by candlelight and a few tears glistened before I knew it.

Valentine's Day soon, and in a month, March 3, your birthday—your sixty-third. Every month, every day, had something for us.

At Women's Club today, for some strange reason, I chose luncheon ticket 63, and I sat across from the Garrett banker's sister and Ethel Murray. You had taught their children and they had all good words for you as a teacher. A Mrs. Clark and Mrs. McDaniels, who sat by me, were so congenial too. It is all very good to be out among people, but coming home and not finding you is another thing. You liked Ruth Fleck—she was lovely on the stage today—is running for recording secretary. We are program committee for the A.A.U.W. coming up soon, so we talked.

I started the car yesterday after finally being able to open the frozen garage door. It started right away—I haven't had it out since before Christmas—it was so sweet. If it hadn't been messy out and 4:00, I might have gone around the block, or more. I took your three gallon can of windshield antifreeze to Standard for half-price. I keep working at sorting out things in the basement and attic.

Nellie and a friend came yesterday. She brought some Christmas gifts and her tax papers. She is going to Florida to visit Mamie in Sarasota. I fixed coffee for them and we sat around the table, three widows.

Shoemaker, who used to ride to the R.R. work with you called—he didn't know, wanted to talk with you, had come across your name while looking for Rainey. Venetta was here—it was on Sunday night—she and I had started with church, dinner, the show "Hair."

"The tender grace of a day that is dead will never come back to me," as Tennyson said.

February 6, 1972

Hi, Harry, gray skies have been sifting snow all day, and my mind has had all it could do to keep from sprinkling tears. Oh,

I know snowflakes sparkle and tears glisten—if there is sun, but today it isn't that way.

Oh, I know the minister's sermon was about "Carry it on," and I will carry it on as bravely as I can before others, but I just want to let you know I can get very blue sometimes. Helen and Harold just came home and had to shovel their way from the garage to the house. It is 5:30—I came in at 3:00 to an empty house. Helen B. and I had a good dinner at Ayres', and a good talk too, I guess. Helen B. never knew love, really; and Helen and Harold, next-door, will eventually come to what we did. It is difficult to "roll with the punches," whatever that means. Am I hugging my grief? Or am I just facing it, freeing myself to go on to whatever new way of life may emerge?

In the fury of wildness, after coming in to be alone, I tossed a white hat I bought for Steve's wedding, and tried on dresses that had been hanging. Out some of them will go with saner thinking—"This I had when Ed and Marvoline were eating out with us; this I had in the lavish fur coat days; this I had but couldn't wear in the recuperative period, etc."

Finally I popped two chocolates into my mouth and made a cup of coffee to sip while I watched the winter Olympics in Sapporo, Japan. Venetta and I watched them till 2:30 a.m. Friday after sewing club. I embroidered on the tablecloth, and she graded papers at the same time we were watching TV. Also we talked about the attitudes of students and ways of teaching. It seems a teacher is bereated, and a nurse is an angel of mercy. After she left, I did the dishes and crawled into bed at 3:30.

Everyone came to sewing club but Ethel, and it was so cold. I told the girls I wasn't serving until it was down to zero, but at two above, I had to. It was good to have laughter and talking in the house. The table was beautiful with mother's lace cloth and the gold candles we never got around to buying before. Valentine napkins, peach melbas, cookies, etc. You always helped me make the table bigger, and you appeared later in the evening. And I gave you of goodies after they had gone, and we gloried in how you had made the house look—the bathroom and maybe the kitchen floor. And often you had shopped for the goodies.

It was a good life, and I am not idealizing or romanticizing. It was was living in "high," and now I find it so difficult to shift into "second."

Here, my mother with her "count your many blessings" intercedes in thought. Of course I have blessings galore you left me with, and I am not unmindful—it is just so difficult to disentangle my yesterdays from my todays, and to become me instead of us. Dad would say, "Everything's going to be all right."

The answer, I suppose, is action and constructive thinking. I will not let this feeling of being unloved and unneeded engulf me. But, all of a sudden, to cease being a romantic wife and an enthusiastic teacher, at the same time, is a pretty big order. Nevertheless, I have to hope that the One who oversees the ordering has plans, if I choose to cooperate. And there is no other choice. I have to find my way, and I have to do it wisely and happily. It will take a lot of listening and keeping in touch with a "higher power." The sun may yet make the snowflakes sparkle and the tears glisten.

February 14, 1972

Dear Harry, this is love's day. The kissing dolls that Gerry gave you when you were ill are on the bookcase. And the "he" has a rose behind his back. They were put there yesterday as I was going through things from the attic. I think I may give them to Tina.

Florence and I went to see Lloyd and Marilyn today. I took two of your "uglies," a green doll with red hair, and a giraffe with a heart on his neck to Lloyd to give to Tina. Her mother called tonight because she wanted one to use on a package for Mabel Houk, who is ill. Great tears rolled down Tina's cheeks—she couldn't part with the green "uglie," but she would give up the giraffe, and I okayed it. I am glad I gave her the gold locket—she treasures it, always putting it in the gift box when she takes it off. Tina will have a sadness greater than any I knew when growing up—her one brother, of three, a mongoloid.

Her daddy's sister has a sadness—a sixteen-year-old daughter, one of three, gave birth to twin girls this morning at home. The doctor across the street took the babies to the hospital. Everybody has something, I guess.

Lloyd seemed more like an adjusted person than anytime since Gerry's death. Was proud of his meat loaf, which I tasted, of his potato salad, and of his roasts. Sometimes, he says, he can hardly stand the loneliness, but neither Gerry nor you were ill so long.

85

He said your quicker way was best, really. There wasn't the gnawing before that he had. Honey, it is dreadful at times to be alone.

Before I tossed a picture of Edward and Mrs. Simpson, I looked at it long. They were forty-two and forty, just a little older than we when we were married eight years after they were. They looked pretty old at seventy-two and seventy. But evidently it was love, and still is.

I am going to have a big bonfire with the things I have tossed out of the attic as soon as the snow goes a bit more. If I can burn also some of the sadness and loneliness, it will be good. But I don't ever want to lose the memory of the great caring we both had, the comfortable togetherness. I suppose that is what makes it so difficult. Anyway at times, I think I can't go on, and then it seems something soothing around me sets me right again. I don't understand it except, "Blessed are they that mourn, for they shall be comforted." It happens again and again.

Your tulips and the crocuses are pushing upward. And today was like spring. Lloyd gave Florence and me each a box of frozen fish he had caught. I ate them all for supper with some potato salad from Maloley's. Oh, there is much to be glad about. I do enjoy some of the time. I miss the mental stimulation of teaching, the happiness of your presence, and I am just not used to being house-bound or in the presence of women so much. I don't like being responsible for the upkeep for our place either. The things that need fixing scare me.

Church yesterday was no comfort. The intern and the young people with long hair and blue jeans took over. What would happen if the untrained took over at the Lincoln Life or at the Fort Wayne National Bank or at the Duemling Clinic? There is something to be said for long years of preparation. I left before services were over and went for a walk in the rain, which was more comforting. At Plymouth Church, where I met Helen, a little boy was eating a donut, and when I talked to him he offered it to me for a bite. That, too, was comforting.

Don't feel too sorry for me. I will find my way through "what I am going through." I suppose it is love's way to wonder if I did as much as I could have and to be sorry for what I did wrong. Just remember that as we lived, I always, always loved, and in togetherness, the worst sometimes shows up along with the best. You know that, of course, and I can almost feel your gathering me to you in glorious acceptance, no matter what.

February 15, 1972

Darling, I have just had a cup of tea with thought, and I want to confide in you again. I have had no contact with anyone by phone, nor have I been outside except to pick up the paper. I rather wanted this week to root around in the attic and elsewhere here at home. There is much to revalue and much to discard.

I found two letters you kept, from me, written on May 28 and 29, 1944. Do you notice the date—our wedding year, and your last days on earth? Also there was one from you to me written on the twenty-eighth and mailed on the twenty-ninth. We had just given up the apartment in the little gray stone house to Walter and Lucile, You had a job between Garrett and Chicago as brakeman on the B. and O. railroad. Good money for you and I could work at W. and D.'s, and we would get married later. My one letter had quick pictures drawn among the sentences—they were a scream. But the love we expressed and the pathos at giving up a summer was good, I suppose. Tears ran freely much of the afternoon, and I flung myself across the bed in weeping abandon several times. The freedom of tears that I couldn't cry before—the hurt was too deep—has helped, unless I have started a waterfall. At the end of one letter I said "home" was in your arms, and it was ever thus. I can't explain it, but the touch of you was so different from the others. It just made me feel your goodness, your cleanness, your aliveness. I would never, never have traded you for anyone else. I would love to live it all over again! What a success you were as a good husband and a wonderful friend! I have had the greatest blessing any woman can have—a lasting love that was shown in multitudinous ways.

I have wished today that I had retired a year sooner. That way I might have lessened the strain for both of us. However, teaching and our way of life was a routine we liked and perhaps, as you often said, it was a wisdom greater than ours that kept the way as it was.

There were snowflakes today, and television, and lighted squares in the neighbors' houses as dusk changed to dark. Now all the drapes are pulled and the locks tight. The house is very still except when the refrigerator hums or the furnace whirrs. I used to say there was no laughter here when we were tired and serious about our work. Now there is no talking. That is just one of the trials on being alone—being dumb so much of the time.

I am not, as you well know, an Alice-sit-by-the-fire. I have got to have movement and action—in what way I do not know, but I must get things in order and I must get busier with living. There must be some reason why I feel this need so strongly that I am not convinced I am as old as I really am. I think I understand Tennyson's Ulysses urge.

February 17, 1972

Darling, it's only 9:30 and I have just gone through a recipe folder tossing out half the clipped recipes. What good stuff I intended to cook for us, and perhaps company. Alas, we were so busy, and we learned to like the common quick foods. But, eating with you was one of our heavens, whether here at home or out in the world.

I worked in the basement and the attic much of today, after calling the Salvation Army and learning a truck could call after 12:30. I got rid of the suitcase Harold gave me and your railroad one. Your brakeman's cap rested alone, clean and beautiful in one drawer. I could not check it out, so I put it in a cellophane bag for now. Out went curtains we had stored, rugs, pillows, a blue wedding blanket, a red lamp we courted by, dishes, and the carpet in the basement. I spent a lot of time on old letters that I hesitate to destroy yet, for they show so much of my other life and might be useful in some writing I might choose to do.

TV took up some of my time. The Nixons are off to China at 10:30, and seeing them so happy together made me cry, now that I can. Also I watched my two shows from 2:00 to 3:00. And the news tonight at 6:00, and *Rapping 'Round* from 7:00 to 8:00.

I folded and put away a big washing I did last night. There was a bath for me last night and a clean bed and clean floors. The sweeper even got a new bag. Oh, and yesterday there was a big "burn-up." I felt as if a lot of my life went up in smoke, old hats, dresses, etc. Florence and Ken think it is illegal to burn trash in the city. Come to think of it, I do not remember seeing anyone else do it. And there's a new trash burner in the basement. That reminds me, I found a browned cigarette half in one of the little planters I gave away today.

Tomorrow is Friday. I go to the beauty shop at 10:15, leave

here at 9:50. I wish life were as zesty as with you, even if sometimes I may have been testy. Goodnight, my dear.

February 18, 1972

Snowflakes chased each other all day, darling, and yet they didn't stack up much. I got my hair fixed and had a good swiss steak dinner followed by lemon meringue pie, and then I came home for TV from 2:00 to 3:00. I had a table for two by the big post where we so often sat. I watched people who were together—it is so good to talk over food. At home I picked up all over the house and made the bed. After a light supper, I watched the news and *Truth or Consequences*. Then I read in a new biography book about Robert and Elizabeth Browning.

In one place there was the line, "When you came, you never went away," and it was always that way with me about you. Sometimes you are even more with me than in life, more poignantly so, indeed. Oh, we talked about how it might be, but that talk was so bland. And the flowers Robert gave Elizabeth—and the roses you grew for me! And when in New York you went to find out if I made the master's exam, and I had with honor, you bought four bunches of flowers on street corners and came to me with the wonder and joy of cheering—I had been almost sick with fear of not making it in English after teaching in the grades so many years. And last year, in Valentine week, you came home with so many hearts of candy (because they were a bargain), I had to give some away. Oh, the tender, loving generosity of you! I will never get over this feeling, and the feeling that perhaps I didn't do enough for you, yet I can think of many times when I did make you happy. I realize that this is a natural feeling, and that one should forgive one's self for any guilt feeling that crops up. I am sorry for any hurt, and I know that you would gladly blot it out, as the young doctor did for Susan Martin on TV when she told her story.

Perhaps I should not be reading a love story that has some resemblance to ours—but I found this line in it, "There is nothing like travel to clear the head and restore mind and heart to health." So I am going to Japan in July. Venetta called me and I called Grace and we talked of the trip and the next meeting for further plans for it. I am going to get busy and try to get recruits for it. Oh, honey, I am a lonely wanderer, but if I am also busy, some of the loneliness will ebb. Strange, I just felt an ebbing, a sort of release. "Don't sit and brood," says one. "Just think of the good," says another. "Keep busy and don't think," says another still. "It takes a lot of crying and praying," offers a remarried widow. Maybe if I let myself feel what really is, and have enough sense not to form a habit of grieving, there will come a form of peace, serenity, love that transcends death and transfers itself to the living, a greater love from our love. There has to be something.

I see you as I left on the plane for the Cleveland Clinic, down there fading away as I floated to help I had to have. It tore the heart out of me to leave you that day. And as I left on the plane for Europe, for the longest vacation we ever had apart, afraid again either I or you might break up our twosome. And again last summer as I left for Europe the second time, there was the bare spot of ground with your metal marker, a vivid reminder that is had at last happened. Tears tugged at my eyes, the tears that finally came in torrents this week.

It will all work out. I will make it work. All that you have left me was so much more when we shared it. But I will not chafe at life or feel sorry for myself, if that is what it is. Grief must give way to gladness, gaiety, and a glowing spirit. Because of the richness of our love, we pay. All love is like that. And you paid in your last knowing, I am paying in my now not-knowing, but I can keep the coins of our payment shining. Yes, that I can do for us, God accepting. So with appreciation for memories of you and your deeds, and with aspiration for effectual living and overcoming sorrow, I go on from day to day. It will work out.

March 2, 1972
Darling, tomorrow is your birthday. And today Mamie has left the sixties. Those dinner parties for your and her birthday were so wonderful.

I have just been thinking about our living together with the crosses on the doors and the crystal doorknobs that I have always loved. Twenty-one years you lived here—in your only home of your own. Sharing it meant so much, and will, because your presence is always felt here, "as the wine must taste of its own grapes."

The tulips are bursting forth to defy the cold winds that have blown all day after yesterday's warmth of about sixty degrees. Three yellow crocuses were out as I walked to the bus. Sticks and papers were on the yard. I can hardly wait to gather them up.

Ah, if you could gather me up in your arms! How I would bloom! I have been reading about Catherine and Peter Marshall in her first book. In many ways he seems like you. She tells of a dream where he was tending the roses he always wanted. You couldn't get enough of them, in the catalogues, in the markets, in your garden. I hope to take better care of them this year. I won't be quite so bewildered.

I went to your beloved doctor Tuesday, the first time since June 7, and he had time to talk and to listen about you. I liked him better than I ever have—I understand your feeling—and I feel so much safer. I was intolerably thirsty so I was tested for sugar. No diabetes. Blood pressure 154 over 90. Is that what yours was? Does he tell everyone that? He said mine had been that the last three times, but I thought it was lower when tested by Dr. Lampe. I walked home pondering about the thirst. It may be the medicine I got at Cleveland, he said, and he let me say it might be the general unrest I feel living in "low gear."

Today I went to the Lincoln Bank V.P. I asked about certificates of deposit, and I went to Verwiebe, the attorney Lebamoff suggested about a will. I want to get things in good order, all the way around.

Aunt Etta died at 2:00 today, so Lloyd and Florence and I will go to Ossian tomorrow night. There is sewing club at Lela's later about 8:00. All of Mother's family are now gone, and all of Dad's.

Helen and Irwin Arnold took me to Ted and Tom's South on Tuesday and then to their house. She is going to Europe with her daughter and granddaughter the fifteenth. Lucile will bring me home from sewing club, and Ruth Fleck called about taking me to Women's Club today but I declined. People are so good, but I must drive more and be independent.

Oh, honey, I have so much to be glad about, as generous you would have me be, but I miss you so. I always wear your ring and I remember your saying that with it I would know a greater security than ever before, and it was so true, so true. Strange, I just had a feeling "all will be well."

March 10, 1972

Hi, Harry, a week ago tonight Florence and Ken took me to Ossian to see Aunt Etta—on your birthday. She looked so beautiful, so natural—Irma had put a poem she wrote called "Autumn" into her folded hands. She never wore any jewelry, and Irma wanted her to go with something in her hands. There were rhinestone buttons on her white dress with tiny black flowers, and lace at the throat and wrists. It was good to talk to Dick. Ethel was there. Lloyd, gray bearded, and Bill and Shirley and Marilyn were there.

The funeral the next day at 2:00 was crowded, and it was difficult for me. A girl sang "In the Garden" and a woman minister preached a beautiful sermon, using much appropriate poetry. It was very cold, snowy, and windy at the cemetery. We stopped at the CharKing in Waynedale afterward and then went to Southtown Mall to shop around. I came in with my groceries and cried out to the walls, my heart ached so.

Venetta called—she was at Southtown Mall and had wanted me to eat with her but couldn't get me, so she ate alone. She came over and I made some coffee and we talked until 9:00.

On Sunday I went to her church with her, and we ate at Frank's. Then she went to her workshop last session at South Wayne. At 5:30 she came back and we had the pie we bought from Frank's at noon, with coffee and fruit salad and cheese and crackers and cashews. On the spur of the moment we went back to her church to hear the Dutch singers, and then to the Spiritualist Church on Wells Street. One began at 6:30, the other at 7:45. Anna Marie Howard, the German nurse from Marion gave the sermon, and Mrs. Brock and she halved the messages. Mrs. B. said Mom and Pop and you came to greet me and bring love, and that my hands were tied now but not for long. Oh, honey, my hands are truly tied. I want to reach out and touch with them.

I have finished *A Man Called Peter* and it had much more meaning than when I first read it. I have worked on my tablecloth since sewing club a week ago tonight after seeing Aunt Etta. It is put away until next club meeting. Tuesday and Thursday I went to the Women's Club, and Wednesday I went to a breakfast at Florence's church. Today I got my hair fixed and had lunch at Ayres'. Tomorrow I should clean house and shop for what Asian food I will take to Sunday's party at Kathy Anders' house. So I have been and will be busy, but with half a heart.

The sunset glowed beneath pink shrouded clouds tonight, and the yellow crocuses were thick against the gray stone at the front of the house, though it is about thirty degrees. I stare at the bare trees and the gray grass. I look in the mirrors and wonder if others guess how my heart hurts, and I promise to smile more but it seems forced. Just for you to be here would be enough, just your warm, real presence.

Your sister Mamie wrote this week—on your birthday; last night I talked on the phone to Woodie and Minnie and Nellie. They said your nephews would be happy to have the three watches, that they were still wearing their graduation watches, and yours are newer. I will also give each a cigarette lighter if desired—there are three left, unless I find more. There are the good handkerchiefs, too.

It is hard to dole out stuff that has been dear. I went to the deposit box to put in a new five-thousand-dollar certificate. I touched the packets of bonds and stocks and certificates and cash, our converted energy, so much of it, and I knew I, as you, could not take it with me, and I was bewildered and bedeviled. I feel shame as I write this because I should be thankful and enjoy security. I just want to share with you the results of our labor. Love is a sharing, the happiest sharing there is, I suppose. I should be glad we shared so much for so long, and I should not be crying.

I remember so many things you said to me about this division of us, and I will try, each time after tears, to smile and work and share and think and enjoy and love. But I knew today I could never love any other man than you. We were in our thirties when we met and loved, the love of maturity and richness and reverence. There have been enough glowing moments to last both lifetimes.

March 16, 1972

Sweetheart, I have never loved you so much as I do at this moment—I feel you very much with me—in the togetherness that bridges death, the togetherness of the spirit. It is as if you are watching, guiding, cheering me. It is as sweet as that day last autumn when you went with me to visit your folks in Garrett, the day I drove I-69. I pray it is as sweet when I go to clear the yard and care for the flowers this spring.

The grass is greening, the trees are starting to put out buds, the tulips are higher, the crocuses stand like Chinese soldiers ready for Nixon, the temperature was forty-two today.

It is my mother's wedding day, her mother's birthday, and to-

93

morrow is her father's birthday. March has memories for me, your birthday and Mamie's, and my father died on March 9, also Aunt Etta was buried on March 4. This may be the birthday of a newer attitude toward being away from you; the desolation, the despair, the death may go.

Yesterday Florence and I did taxes, ate at Richard's with Ken at noon, and last night I read and watched Billy Graham on TV. He was preaching in Chicago, beautiful Norma Zimmer sang. I read *To Live Again* by Catherine Marshall and was most interested in the chapters "They Walk in Wistfulness" and "Is There Life After Death?" I also read "Thumbelina" in a book of Hans Christian Anderson stories, which suggested a transformation of spirit to me. From recent reading of an N.R.T.A. magazine, I was challenged by the successor of Freud who kept his wife's image ever present in difficulty though she was killed when the Germans overran Austria. What anguish some people have to bear and conquer!

Darling, I have been very busy. Venetta and I met at church Sunday, then we came home to get my almond cookies, rice pudding, Hawaiian vegetables, and Hawaiian dessert to take to a "Lillich" party at Kathy Anders'. But first we picked up Grace and Freida and had a light lunch at Hobby Ranch. At 3:00 Joe began the meeting and then we women got our foreign food ready. It was all so wonderful with the punch and wine and general geniality and picture taking and picture showing. Outside the lightning flashed and the thunder bombed and the rain gushed, but we were in a big beautiful house. Leaving, we sank in "quicksand" mud, and once in the cars raced through the waterfall. Venetta and I stopped at the farmhouse of her aunt, Ethel's sister, awhile.

On Tuesday in the cold fogginess I went downtown at 3:20, and Venetta and I went to a Lenten supper at the church, then to the library. Malinda Wade, a black girl, the president of her class at Northrup, talked to me, and a boy from Elmhurst told me about his term paper combining three religious books, *The Razor's Edge*, *A Man Called Peter*, and *Seven Story Mountain*, I believe it was. I was at home, in tune, with these two, who talked so naturally with me. My teaching, my marriage, two closed doors now. (Perhaps God can open two others.) Bang! Bang! They went shut and at the same time. What a mighty wind and what a mighty sound has echoed and re-echoed since!

Today at the Women's Club were lovely film pictures of Africa—flowers, animals, houses, scenes, people. Lucile and I enjoyed a luncheon and then went to an Indiana Retired Teachers' meeting. It was in regard to the teachers' pension. You see I keep busy. And tomorrow evening Helen B. and I are going to a Bethlehem Church supper. It is also the day to get my hair fixed at 10:15.

The table is pretty with a dark green cloth and a lone green candle in a glass holder. I want the home to be pretty, and I want to be pretty. I am glad we so often ate by candlelight. And that we so often held each other tight. And that you said "I love you" so easily. And for the way you said my name, and for "Good night, Irene."

March 29, 1972

Oh, my dear, it is exactly ten months since I felt your hand reassure mine with continual pressures and then still to limpness, since I pressed those last two kisses on your brow above your closed eyes. On TV tonight the gates of East Germany opened to let West Germans greet friends and relatives they hadn't seen for six years. I was there rushing to you to be enfolded by your arms and to feel your cheek against mine.

Marvoline and Lucile had lunch with me at Jonelli's today, and it was a delightful two hours. She is caring for Ed's mother at the Allen County Nursing Home, and is an ambassador for Ed, as I am for you. It is a comforting thought that we carry on and act for husbands who must be away awhile. A snatch of radio music this morning ran "till my trophies at last I lay down." And I thought of all the trophies, the rose prize ribbons, your high school ring—your treasures, large and small, that I have had to hold and cherish and decide about.

Last Sunday, Danny came about 4:00 and stayed till 8:00 while Woodice studied at the I.U. library. I gave him the Swiss watch I bought for you in Zurich, and handkerchiefs and other things. We talked more than we ever have, and I served raspberry sherbert and Chinese cookies and coffee while we talked about his college teaching and his new home and his wife.

The Sunday before, Steve and Linda came with the two little boys, and I gave them some of your things and the gold-faced

Bulova watch. Eric and Jamie wanted hamburgers and french fries and cokes, so we went to the CharKing in Steve's new red Dodge and had a cozy time. When they left, Eric said, "Good-by, Grandma."

I cleared out your bedroom chest of drawers and put what is left of your trophies in the bottom drawers. I have a watch for Bobbie yet. I have cast out so many things of my own, too, that the three top drawers in your chest now stand empty like my arms, my heart. I do want order, I guess I do. Oh, honey, I feel shame and wickedness in yearning for turned-back months and the wild chaos of busy and happy living and sharing. I remember how many times we were allowed to rebuild after our togetherness was threatened, and I recoil at the greed of wanting it to last forever instead of "until death do us part." So I shall try to learn to go on as you said you wanted me to. In that respect, I am afraid I have been a slow learner.

Venetta and her mother and I were with Florence and Ken last night for pictures of Europe and music. Tomorrow the people from Indianapolis stop at the Hobby Ranch on the way to Detroit. Venetta and I will have lunch with them and try to plan Hawaii and Japan with them. Last Saturday night Venetta came when I was making Chinese cookies, and afterward we went to Zoli's for wine and pizza and salad and coffee—no wonder Robert Kennedy liked the place. Oh, honey, there seems to be no dearth of what-to-do, and I have so much to be thankful for. Leona Plumanns called tonight. She and Bernie are taking me to Lucile's at 1:00 for Easter dinner. Everyone is so good really. And I talked to Lloyd twice one day this week. There is always Helen B. to go to church with.

Last Sunday I chose to drive, the first time this year, to your chapel service. I even wore the driving gloves I bought for winter and neglected, and I even got into the garage without too much trouble. There was beautiful snow Monday, and today it rained and iced the trees and bushes and eaves. There must be a lot of driving this summer.

The house seems so still—sometimes the wind sounds or a car goes by. I pulled the curtains apart awhile ago and every house on the west side of Reed toward Rudisill had golden windows, lights aglow. I still have supper by candlelight, as we used to do, and as the neighbors said always looked so pretty, but I remember

96

to pull the drapes, lest eating alone that way seem too conspicuous. I do not want to accentuate my loneliness, and my tears, when they finally come, have been secret tears.

A long procession of happy memories just floated by, Columbia University days, courtship days, apartment days, school days, holidays of travel, days in our own home; and, yes, there were all the nights, too, nights of love and waking up together, I guess I was "the most loved woman in Fort Wayne," as you sometimes said, and as you so often showed me.

Why cry? Even if ten months stretches into ten years, more or less?

April 3, 1972

Hi, Harry, I just watched *Laugh In* because you always got a kick out of it. And then I looked out as I turned it off to see if it was still raining—it is, very much so, a continuing rain. But it was nice at 1:00 when Florence and I drove to Hoagland.

Marilyn had new carpet and her house seemed so cozy—four yellow placemats on the table in the yellow and green dining room—a pretty Easter centerpiece. The little man she keeps for his teacher-mother wandered all around, dark-eyed and tall for his age. She served a dessert we copied and coffee.

Then after we went to the bank, we stopped at Lloyd's. How good to have a brother! He was asleep, but he got up and showed three reels of home movies. There I was stepping it off so sprightly to the plane for Europe last summer. And there you were, honey, in your pretty green sport shirt and I in my brown and white dress, the striped one of 1970. How happy you looked as you and I were getting into our Ford! I could see it plain as day, the look in both of our faces because we had each other, the look others noticed, the glowing look. There were pictures of Gerry, so natural, so at home with her brood. I am telling you I miss you two! Lloyd served cherry cake with chocolate icing and ice cream. His house looked neater than mine, but you know me. In two shakes, with inspiration, I can haloize mine—ready for company. Oh, if you were coming home! What heaven!

Lloyd gave me the most life-like snapshot of you, sitting at ease in his back yard in 1970. It is probably the best picture I have of you. Lloyd, in his gray beard, and Dave, in his bushy black beard! But how good it was to be there! I think the Hoagland days are

97

in June. And Lloyd had all his children and grandchildren home for Easter.

Lucile and Walter invited me yesterday for a beautiful time. There were nine altogether for a ham, sweet potato, brocolli dinner with all the delightful trimmings and lovely decorations. They have been so very good to me.

Venetta and I saw *The Godfather* Saturday and ate at the Bonanza afterward where we joined Walt and Lucile. We had had shopped and stopped at the M.C.L. for lunch. She, too, has been so good to me.

On Thursday we joined Phil and Hope and Marian and Elaine for lunch at Glenbrook Ayres' Store. Hope had bought a beautiful new blue dress at Ayres' and was wearing it. Venetta got a white and navy one Saturday. It is Asia this summer for us, I guess. Last night I taxied to the Hobby Ranch at 6:00 to have dessert with Phil and Hope and Marian, who were on the way to Indianapolis from Detroit. It is so good to have friends, real friends. Grace and I are playing bridge at her sister's on Wednesday. The past two summers in Europe have enriched my life so—but not in comparison to our U.S.A. travels together. You know that, surely. I have so much less now that I must indeed make more of it. And in sorrow any ray of light becomes a rainbow.

I hear the rain dropping on the roof, and I think how into each life some rain must fall and tears must come, and I ache and I wonder as I "walk through the valley of the shadow." The comfort always comes, and the soul growth, I suppose, but oh, the pain of change! I cannot live without you, my dear, but yet a while I can.

Through me, you and I must tidy up our gifts of life and love and work and wealth before we are truly free together, wherever that may be. What will be, will be.

April 18, 1972

Darling, today is Tuesday, a day for Women's Club and Retired Teachers. How utterly strange in comparison to a year ago in the classroom and you at eventide! How foreign to the years of work and love!

Yesterday I changed the title to the car and got a new license plate. I took the third treatment from Dr. Mueller for nosebleeds. I went to Klaen's Home to see John Ruhl's wife, a slender little lady with a widow's peak, lying among her flowers. And I remembered John giving me a wrist watch before a dresser at Katy Dorwin's home before I went back to college my first summer at Ball State. After a dinner at Ayres' I came home to clean the car windows, and I hurt my back. I thought I might have to stay in the back seat until some one found me. But I got to bed and flattened out. Later I took a hot shower, which seemed to help, and dressed for the Rachel Circle at church. Gladys Stanner brought me home in her new Oldsmobile.

Venetta and I saw Ladonna Huntley in *Diary of Anne Frank* at the Civic Theater Saturday night after a light supper at the CharKing with Walt and Lucile. Sunday we met at church and then joined Hope and two friends at the Hobby Ranch before going to Grace Lloyd's for the Cheer Group meeting to discuss the summer trip. A rainy, rainy day. Home after supper with Venetta at Atz's.

Florence and Ken are in Florida visiting his brother and a sister in Key West. They were here for supper Wednesday. I had huge luscious strawberries for dessert with angel food cake. I remember how you liked fresh strawberries.

I just had a cheese toastie for supper. I remember how you appreciated cheese toasties, and how you always said a special thank-you for French toast on a Saturday morning. I never got tired of fixing meals for us, or of washing the dishes afterward. I loved doing for us.

And the cleaning we did together! I have looked at the bare kitchen windows so often. I do not know how to handle the storm windows. And I am afraid I might hurt my back really bad. The curtains are dry cleaned. I considered calling Florence's Mexican neighbor who does housework four hours a day. Oh, if we could do it together! We did so much cleaning, and we enjoyed it so much—the results, especially. Daily living together was so rewarding.

The maple tree has red leaves, the locust tree has white buds, the orange bush has green points, and the hedge is greener every day. Dad's Madonna lilies are up six inches, and some roses are coming to life. The grass will soon clamor for the mower, and yes, the tulips have red edgings. There have been so many April showers, and two days of bright sunshine have urged nature to surge. I wonder if I can cope with the yard, the cleaning of the house, the car, and the many places to go. I pray I can take things in my stride and stay well.

Everything meant so much more to me when we shared it. Perhaps I've said this before, but I have to say it again. A tulip bud, a book shelf, clean curtains, candle light, a pretty table, a freshly made bed, all lovely, lovely things in a home are best when shared. Memories caress but they lack the kiss of life.

I wish I could sit on the stool in the basement while you took a shower, make a pot of coffee while you sat on the white kitchen chair, stand still while you zippered my dress, or watch you plant a rose bush or paint the garage. The cozy, homey togetherness of life. The making up after a quarrel. The concern and caring for the one who is ill. The comforting of the disappointed or injured spirit. Love, sweet love, is what the world needs, and how few understand, or seem to understand, what they could have, or have, until it is late, late. And then they see it as it might have been, but perhaps it is wisdom's way to protect us from too much ecstasy. And time's way to mist the memories.

Oh, darling, to rush into the enclosure of your arms and to erase any need for words!

April 19, 1972

Oh, Harry, I just have to mention the tulips—there is a big red one and a yellow one splashed with red in a green glass on the dinette table. They glowed in candlelight as I enjoyed my soup and pink applesauce at supper. The raindrops have renewed their vigor on the roof—they have danced the live long day. I got out into the back yard briefly and saw so many new rose shoots. There is going to be a lot of work I wish you could do.

Your sister Nellie just called to invite me to dinner Sunday—Bob's birthday—but I am tied up with the Asian Tour meeting.

This was no day to wash the kitchen windows, so I decided to try to get your box of papers in order, finally, after some previous tries. The college records are filed in order, the teaching licenses, the letters of honor, the taxes from 1945 on, the hospital bills, the insurance papers, etc. All that study, work, and suffering. But there was pride too, and the joy of accomplishment, and the sweet recovery from illness.

Your *Reader's Digest* book came and I read "Bring Me a Unicorn," about Anne Lindbergh and Charles. I would do everything today in shifts, not too much of one thing at a time. A feeling of restlessness tugged at me all day. I know, I understand how love comes to the young as tulips bloom and how love lasts, if we appreciate, until fading time for first one tulip, then another. It will be thus for Anne and Charles. Anne didn't want to be wished happiness—she wanted courage and strength and a sense of humor for life with Charles. Perhaps I can wish myself those three attributes and go on seemingly serene. I wonder if it is as hard for most people as it is for me—to be without the one I loved above all others, to be without the truest friend I ever had. I was so at home with you, so in tune, so for you always. What I felt for you was beyond the wildest hopes of youth.

Nevertheless, I pledge again this night, not to wallow in self-pity and thoughts of loss, but to be busy and to work out a worthwhile existence. Of course, I will naturally remember, but with happiness, I hope, and with thankfulness for the life that was ours. I think we both had far more joy than we ever dreamed—because we found each other. Courage, at times, yes. Strength also. Humor, maybe we could have profited with more—a provocative word—Come, humor!

May 2, 1972

Oh, Harry, I just looked at the end of the last entry about humor, and I remembered a recent sermon by Rev. Mather in which he said humor and insight went together. How important the two qualities are, and how I wish we could laugh and see into things together. It is so different to laugh alone and look ahead alone. But I shall keep on trying—and with people, too.

Honey, Bill Pomp's father called and took me out to dinner Saturday night at the Shrine, the first time in exactly eleven months that I haven't been the extra woman. You liked his son, Bill, and his wife, Esther, was so lovely—five years she has been gone. Perhaps it was because I knew his son so well at Central when he was president of his class twice, and his wife also treasurer of the Central P.T.A., that I felt so at home with him. And I had cried when I hung up the receiver after saying yes. And I am near tears now, but it was so new to me, being with someone other than you. He said, "Esther would be so happy if she could know." I wonder. He called last night and said the evening went so fast and that he would help me with the car. He sold cars and worked at the G.E. most of his life.

Today I drove out to our marker at New Haven and I stopped at Gardner's for a sandwich and coffee and met John Bardon. He, too, insists on helping me with driving and suggested Columbia City next Monday or Tuesday because I am busy every day the rest of the week. Yesterday I drove out to Lloyd's and gave him the new book, *Grief*, which came out in April. I have read it through twice.

One way of therapy the small book suggested was to write it—anything but dam it up. And to realize that gradually ties would have to break and life go on in a different way. At the Women's Club, Thursday, Ruth Fleck said I had done unusually well in adjusting and getting out and about. At times there is a deep hurt that takes possession of all of me if I am true to myself. But, honey, I do try.

Florence just called—got home at 7:45—sixteen days of Florida trip. Marilyn has surgery Friday at 11:00. Val graduated in nursing Sunday.

I voted today at the primary and will listen to returns at 9:30 in half an hour. Lucile just called and I have three dates with her for places to go. So you see I am busy, and as you said, she is my best friend.

Hope and Welcome were here the twenty-third to go to church with me and to Ayres' for dinner and to Dr. Lillich's at 3:30. Venetta and Grace and I ate out about 10:30 after the meeting and after the talk about Joe's future job. Hope is so wonderful—Venetta and Grace and I are going to Indianapolis June 2 to visit with Hope and Phil. Helen B. and I went to church and to Ayres' for dinner last Sunday.

I have mowed the lawn and tried to keep the house clean. And I have tried to keep from being sad and too lonely. I must trim the roses down. The tulips are beautiful. The merry month of May is so filled with memories and the last love of you. Bless me, be with me, as I go on riding the merry-go-round of life . . . and help me to live it to the fullest . . . what is left.

May 19, 1972

Honey, if ever I loved you, it is truly now. I cried after I came home from town this afternoon, cried myself to sleep finally. I talked to the nicest man while waiting for my bus. He was telling me how he had done his lawn with Scott's Plus 2, and how he was teaching his wife gradually, without telling her, to be a widow. Then I watched TV, and a twin brother and sister, widowed, were talking about what it had meant to both to lose their mates. I couldn't mow my lawn because men were making a cement patio next-door and the big cement mixer was out by the back yard. I got a letter from Internal Revenue about no credit for our estimated taxes, so I hunted the checks, called the local I.R.S. about how to proceed, and then wrote the letter to cancel the unowed bill and penalty and interest. Then I flopped on the bed after I had gathered up all the scattered checks and tax papers, and I let loose.

Tuesday I had gone to the doctor and told him about Bill and me and the episode in the study in front of all the books, with the lights on, and with all our clothes on—not your doctor, mine. And he was very kind and helpful and talked about the beautiful relationship we might have, and perhaps even a happy marriage based on a twenty-year awareness of our two families always knowing of each other. Bill will be in Alaska in July and I will be in Japan in August. That gives us about six weeks, and Bill is rushing me. So I guess I had enough to cry about.

This was a big week. John Bardon took me driving Tuesday, but Bill came in the evening and every evening since. Wednesday I drove to Bluffton with him and to Lloyd's and to Marilyn's where Florence was. I ate at his house twice in the evenings, and he's been here. Walter and Lucile have been with Bill and me, too. Tomorrow Bill is fixing steaks at his house. He's a Johnny Cash sort of man. His voice heals me and he loosens and frees me. We went to your grave and to Esther's grave the same evening this week. Honey, Bill just called again, and I don't think he knew I was crying. He wanted to straighten out something he had said about Florence so he could sleep better. He has a sense of goodness, but oh, I wish he didn't drink and smoke so much.

Now you know. It is ten days till the end of the first year, and there has only been Bill. And, of course, I don't know how it will end, or how I want it to be. I am just not very gay tonight, so I suppose I had better get ready for bed. Good night, honey. I pass it on to you, from Bill to me.

May 31, 1972

Hi, honey, a year ago, your last whole day on earth. I thought of you many times today—I brushed the dust off your picture when I cleaned the bedroom and I thought how many of our plans had collapsed. My whole body squeezed back tears different times during the day. It is better being a widow than never having been a wife, I suppose.

Bill and I agreed not to drive to Bluffton for lunch nor to see each other tonight. But that was at nine in the morning, and at three in the afternoon he called when I had my hand on the phone to call him to come for supper at 7:00 and stay till 10:00. He wrangled an extra half-hour earlier to take the white garage door paint off my right front fender. We two know what it is about, the losing of a mate.

A week ago, almost, I got awfully sore from the estrogen therapy and the doctor canceled it out as did Dr. Porter when I gained fifteen pounds in three weeks. Bill is kind, and he tucked me in when I was so sick Sunday I cried. No one has seen me cry for ages, but you. Bernie had the same trouble when she took the same medicine. She and Leona and Marcia and Terry and I enjoyed a "cook-in" Monday because of the rain. The Beckmans have been so very, very good to me. This was the "kids' " do.

Bill and I ate at his house last night and he really fixed good steaks. We came home to watch a Billy Graham crusade. Oh, honey, I keep living on, keeping love alive, and praying about all.

June 20, 1972

Harry, my dear, June is on its way out, and there has been so much. June seventeenth was the day our mothers were buried, yours thirty-one years ago, mine eighteen years. I wanted to go to both graves of our parents, but I went to Dr. Lillich's meeting about Tokyo on Sunday and had the beauty shop and Bill on Saturday. I just have to keep trying to get everything done. There seems to be twice as much without you. And it is twice as difficult.

The birthday bushes have bloomed and they were lovely. I took Bill and Walt and Lucile and Marcia and Terry to Ye Olde Inn for steaks at the round table, and it was very merry. At home I served a Richard's pink cake and vanilla ice cream with red raspberries. Coffee, of course. When I put the candles on the cake, I remembered the last party you helped me have after the Carousal dinner. Dave was here, and in the fall he and Walt both had heart attacks. My fingers trembled. but I got the ten candles in rosebud holders, and Bill insisted they burn while we ate our ice cream. Of course there was a song, and Walter and I blew out the candles, and I don't remember what I wished. Oh, honey, without you, without Dave's family, it is not the same—it is a blend of the old and the new life I have to live. There were cards with notes from your sisters, and a card with a check from Bill.

The following week I saw Bill every day but Monday. To Bluffton, to Lloyd's, to Bill's house, to the lakes. So for two days I have halted the rush, and tonight he called and so I am cooking supper for two tomorrow night. It is so much easier and happier to cook for two, and if a good woman and a good man bear the loss of their loved ones together—and comfort each other is what time they have, and in what ways they have, does God frown? We have stood by Esther's grave twice, and also by yours.

I find myself crying, I have missed you so lately. This morning I finished reading *Grief*, by Sarah Morris. I had loaned it to my brother, and I wanted to glean what I could again. She talks about breaking the old ties and building anew. It is not easy. I also read "My Kind of Man" in a leaflet from Venetta's church. The author, Joyce Landorf, says a man has to be tough and tender. The tenderness is necessary if she is to be a whole woman. "I die without little things—quiet talks and tender touches."

I appreciate you so much when I care for the yard. I got so sweaty today and yesterday, pulling weeds, setting out little plants, trimming the hedge, cutting off dead roses. And the mowing isn't even done, nor the spaces fixed where roses died out. But I can see how you enjoyed it, and how good the showers felt after the exercise. Just before my shower today, I almost cleaned the basement, until I realized what a tremendous task it would be. Instead I showered and went to the hospital to see Woodie, who has had a prostate operation.

Minnie was there as she was when I went last Wednesday, and he is not doing too well, not healing as he should. Danny is taking care of the dairy and teaching summer classes too. Minnie is going back to work tomorrow.

Little Diane Nahrwold got a wild ride when she asked me to take her to work last week at the busiest time of the day. Her daddy was at the Harvester, because of the strike—older ones called back. But I intend to keep driving, to try somehow to get it all done, and to keep your pride in me.

July 17, 1972

Oh, Harry, the bitter ache of loneliness tugged at my heart today—loneliness only for the presence of you, only you. The roses and the yard need you, the garage needs you, everything around here needs you. The treasures we gathered together mean so little without you. Nothing is really much unless it is shared. There is so much I do not understand about stuff in the garage for the yard, plant food, etc.

A week from today I will be in Tokyo. Grace and Joe talked with me today about arrangements—we are leaving from Indianapolis. Venetta and I said good-by to her aunt in Ossian Saturday and ate at the Dutch Mill. I would love Tokyo if I could come home to you and a beautiful yard and garden. I would cook you a meal fit for a king and I'd love you and clean and tell you all those wonderful things I have really always thought about you.

I drove Bill to the airport last Tuesday for Seattle, where his son lives. He puts laughter in the house, but he is not you. I was with John R. last Thursday—he lost his wife April 14—a nice evening ending at Florence's, but he is not Bill. Today a travel booklet came from John in the mail along with a pretty pin and several hankies, his wife's things.

I have to be me—finally me, though I hate it. I am I, and I must merge with all about me. I must drive down Clinton Street or wherever I want to go. I must eat alone or invite someone in. I must solve the problems or give up. I have got to keep up with life though I ache and tears come. I must push them aside for smiles and good cheer. So, it is Tokyo, here I come, but no matter where I go, my heart will hunger for you, sweetheart.

Now I am going to get busy with odds and ends of house and suitcase, the details of a woman alone, a woman who is searching for something, call it heart's ease, or whatever you will—maybe the search is second best to the finding.

July 21, 1972

Honey, this is it—the last night before the day of the flight for Los Angeles and Tokyo. I am packed and I have everything I need: Florence and Ken to look after the house, Nahrwolds to look after the yard, Jon to take Venetta and me to Dr. Lillich's house. A night's rest and then a morning to check the way I am leaving things. Minnie and Shirley called yesterday inviting me to a ham supper. Mamie sent a card, Nellie phoned tonight. Marcia brought me a travel diary. Florence and Ken were here tonight. I feel good and in tune with my people and yours.

I left my rings you gave me in the deposit box, also mother's diamond and my Swiss watch. This is a different world I am living in—I may be lost without your wedding band. I am going to wear the cameo I bought in Rome, a symbol of a woman standing out boldly against her background, a woman alone. It has been very difficult and I wonder sometimes how I came through the past year, but there were such wonderful people, and the blessed spirit of you and a divine power backing my will to come through, even as so many others have had to do. As Bill says so often, "God has been good to me, honey."

On the bus coming home from town today, I knew I had truly loved and gave thanks for the many finenesses of our relationship. No one can ever be to me what you have been—I do not think I will marry again. I believe I can take each day and be happy and grateful and courageous. Bill has helped. He has loosened and relaxed me and put laughter into my life. It is so easy to talk to him and he is tender and comforting. Maybe he blows smoke in my face and "bottoms up" the beer bottles, and I am afraid he has a charm women see before men do, but he has taught me so much about the car and given me a different slant on life.

But John is—John R.—a desperate person, too close to his sorrow, and he is trying to pressure me into marriage and being his, even after one date. The telephone has been a surprising medium of exchange. As for John Bardon, well, he is a drop-out, his eight or ten calls left me a little weak.

It all makes me almost willing to settle for being an independent person, a cameo individual. Perhaps I should work at the poetry and short stores I keep dreaming about. My career and my wifehood gone, I need something different and powerful. The trip to Asia may be a needed bridge to a final adjustment of the various aches and sorrows and changes of the past year. Last summer as the plane took off, there was that bare spot of earth imprinted on my heart; this year your ring is in the deposit box. They say old ties must be broken, a new way must come. I seem to feel a personal strength and courage coming my way. I trust I can take hold of life and live it with the honor and pride you would wish. There is so much I want to be able to do. I trust God will send me the inspiration and wisdom to choose wisely the worthwhileness of whatever comes my way, through me will continue the worthwhileness of your existence.

September 15, 1972

Honey, I came back the 14th of August. It was raining when Elizabeth Lillich and Mike brought me here at 7:00 p.m. I was tired and I became very lonely in our home. A month ago today was my first whole day resuming ordinary life after the exotic tour of the Orient. You were with me often as I savored sights and sounds and delicious food. Beautiful shrines and forests and cities and courteous dark-eyed people. Oh, Harry, to have shared it with you as I watched other husbands and wives!

But Venetta was, as always, a delightful companion. And I met Mathilde who helped me think about life in a religious sense. And Barbara and her plucky mother from Elwood. Sandy and Frieda were always around, Sandy, the spendthrift, who bought material for her wedding gown in Manilla, and Frieda who will make it. The couple from Indianapolis, the Irwins; and big wonderful Dr. Lillich, the Joe that you liked, completed our group. These were the ten, our ten, who became very close. Nineteen others completed our whole tour, but they were something else—Jewish couples; and a younger set—Sam and the five girls; and eighty-three-year-old Margaret of the three dead husbands. Oh, Harry, I loved it and I bought clothes and two rings, a jade and an alexandrite. You appreciated clothes and jewelry. People don't realize how they dress for each other. To hear you admire something was to treasure it and love you.

Bill came home from Seattle on the 18th of August, and I had to scuttle John out on Wednesday before. It was not easy. He had our marriage planned and did not accept a no, so there was a following phone call and a final letter exchange. Bill and I are "at home" with each other. Bill had much to tell me of his six weeks in Alaska with his son. Bill is so different from you—Kennedy and Onassis come to my mind, but should they? Let's just say it this way: Bill and I can talk so very freely, there are no walls.

He gives me laughter, and freedom from all the barren world of the women. He is a friend, but oh, I don't want to marry. At least I don't think I do. It hurts and it troubles me to thus concern myself, so suppose we just let the matter rest for the present.

Harry, yesterday Lucile, Ethel, and I drove to Arcadia to see Helen because Dave Hartley died. He looked so nice—had a heart attack the Saturday before Labor Day. Memorial Day of 1971 came back to me very clearly as I sat in the funeral parlor and visited with Helen. He was sixty-four—you would be sixty-four in March.

Last week I spent two days working outside. The yard had to be mowed and I fertilized the roses. They miss you. Mr. N. trimmed the hedge. It has rained quite a bit since then. There's a leak in the roof over the front porch, or at least it drips. The windows aren't washed. The five closets are in order because I hid the watch you gave me too well—found it back of the bath towels in the hall closet. May wash the bathroom soon. Everything misses you. Finally got the refrigerator washed inside. There is so much work—when we did it together it took half the time. And how we enjoyed doing it!

I do want everything in order because I see so clearly what can happen. Oh, honey, I am so thankful to be well and strong enough to look after all you and I struggled for. I hope and pray I can cope with all the problems.

The first Sunday after I came home, I got up too late for ten o'clock church, so I went out to your grave and then drove seventy miles out east of New Haven and back. Then I went with Florence and Ken and three others to Spencerville there the Sunday school class had a potluck and homemade ice cream at the Amstutz farm.

There is no lack of places to go. Possibly that is why I don't get my work done. But I know your attitude about that. And, of course, there's Bill in addition to all the other activities and church. When I stop to recount the many get-togethers I have had in the past month since coming from the Orient, I know it would take a book to tell them all. I am so full of wanting to feel your arms about me, and of knowing the sweet peace of your presence.

I will simply have to get up and do the day's dishes. Then perhaps I'll straighten a drawer or two. It all helps the tugs at my heart. And by and by, everything may be in order. Or, is chaos more exciting?

October 23, 1972

Honey, you have been very close to me all day. Our maple tree we replanted at night is going to be one of the red kind, so beautiful in autumn. The locust is a skeleton, and Saturday I picked up five buckets of sticks and leaves, and there are more. It seems you should walk across the lawn with your gentle, easy way of making it more beautiful and better.

I went through every drawer and shelf in the bathroom today. Oh, to see your 'p.j.'s hanging back of the door! And your stuff everywhere—there was always room for both of us—we always managed—now my stuff is spread everywhere, lonesome like.

I even took out the aluminum foil you put in the space under the sink and lined it with cupboard paper and got rid of the nonessentials. Oh, to have you approve it!

All day I picked up and examined the house. Tonight I called Borshelt to check the furnace, and he remarked about how well you had kept it up. I will be home another day and a half—go with Venetta to her church's Hawaiian banquet tomorrow, and play bridge with Florence Wednesday afternoon, and to Women's Club with Lucile Thursday morning. Will hear Robert Frost's daughter speak. Oh, I keep on here, and I go there.

But I know now that it will ever be thus—I miss you more than I can tell anyone. I sat in your pew at chapel before church Sunday and heard a book review, *Bury My Heart at Wounded Knee*. Yes, I drove through continuous rain. You might be proud of me, but oh, to see it in your eyes!

There is the last rose of summer, red and velvety, on the table. We have had early frosts this year. I told Bill how you always arranged the flowers in vases. We are two late roses, blooming awhile, but lonely for you and Esther. We rattle around in our empty houses—he phoned this noon. It is early, four months, to say how it will go, or is it later than we think? I made cookies over his sister's recipe and sent some home with him; also I took Florence and Ken some this morning.

Venetta and I went to Indianapolis to see Phil in a play, *Bus Stop,* last weekend, and Hope and Welcome were with us. Stayed all night with them. Venetta and I also saw Jean Davenport in *The Night Thoreau Spent in Jail* on Friday night after dinner at Ayres'. Oh, Harry, there is so much to tell about, and talk with you was never trivial. You see, I am making the effort, I am

110

living, I am loving. It is such a different phase and I try to keep the sadness out, but it seeps in, always will, I suppose. When it threatens to saturate, I remember roses and books and pajamas and cookies and all the dear togethernesses. And I say, "Forgive me for the times I was difficult." If people could only have a preview of what it is like to be alone after a happy marriage, how few would be the difficult times!

Harry, Woodie has terminal cancer. I am so sorry for Minnie. They have to sell or shut up the dairy. I went to see him in the hospital twice. He told me himself about it and how his bladder had to be removed. We knew a lot of illnesses—yes, we did, but not that bad.

Ruth and Fritz are here in their mobile home on Sandpoint Road. Twenty-eight years ago, come Thursday, they went with us to repeat our marriage vows. It was good to be with them—they both look very well and are going to Florida and way down into Mexico before going back to California.

Honey, you have been so close all day. Life with you and life with young people was so exciting. I felt so needed and was so ready to give. Now it is so-so unless I make the effort, but the natural spring is somewhere else.

January 28, 1973

Oh, Harry, I cried when five days ago I came back and looked at the last entry in this record—three months had passed. It isn't that I haven't thought of you, for I have—every day. Life was just too full to sit down and remember in writing. That, I suppose, is good, but I remember in my heart with pride and joy and tears, and I always will.

Last night Venetta and I, after seeing a show, *American Wilderness*, at the Clyde Theatre, and after talking with Miles Davis at his pharmacy, and after grocery shopping, went to the Paramount for supper. Frank Forsythe of the cemetery was there with his wife and he came over and talked to four women at the next table. I put my hand on his arm to ask if the bridge near the cemetery was remade, and it is—so I shall come out when the weather is fit. One of the women was Grace Harding and you would know the others for they knew you and your roses. Grace had returned from the South Pacific in October, and, honey, I have just come back from London.

111

It was wonderful to spend nine days in London with the perfect forty degree temperatures and a good crowd. Dr. Lillich and Bill Hart, and Joe's new colleague, and a Mr. Schwartz, fiancee of Carol Heyn, and Iris Latham, and Elizabeth Roesler, my roommate, made the eight of us. Three shows, three pubs, three museums and galleries, Harrod's store, the Tower of London, etc., were the way Elizabeth and I went. We had a beautiful hotel, the Royal Horseguards, where there was always good food and a royal welcome in the gay red decor. The Thames from our windows and the buildings opposite were wonderful. And we had dinner with two actresses at a fine restaurant near Covent Garden after a show. One of the girls was an I.U. graduate in 1965, the Magnolia of *Showboat*.

Oh, Harry, I got through our wedding anniversary, October 26, and through Thanksgiving, and through Christmas and New Year's. Bill has been with me often, and he and I were at Marilyn's for a Christmas party on the twenty-third with all of Florence's family. Bill and I went to Lloyd's an hour that night to his family party. I gave each of my six nephews and nieces fifty dollars and each of your four one-hundred dollars. And it was fun, as you once said, to see the response and hear what they would do with it. I gave Bill a shirt and brought him a tie from London. He wants me to see that he is buried with that tie on. Can you imagine? I told him it was to wear with happiness in living.

Oh, honey, I had pretty clothes to wear in London, a new bronze all-weather coat and orange, brown, bronze, and beige dresses, and scarfs—everything just right. How I wish you could have seen me to tell me I looked nice, because for your pride I liked to look nice. And how I wish I could again help you with a new suit, or a shirt or tie!

Venetta and I had breakfast here today and heard a Presbyterian program on TV. Then we went to church and to dinner at Ayres'. We shopped afterward and I brought home two dresses—will decide on one. I also bought a book on Maria Theresa of Austria. My horizon has widened as my heart has stretched—I know so much more of the world and of the greatest sorrow there can be—anyway it is the greatest sorrow I have ever known. And yet, I thank God often because I was with you at the end.

Honey, the snow is falling, the slush is freezing, the grayness is gathering. Winter may really be settling. But the war, the awful war is ended by one day. As I think of the war, I will always think of two young men I taught who lost their lives so very soon after going to Viet Nam.

Shortly after I came home from London I had Walter and Lucile here at the house for supper. They had taken me to Ye Old Inn before I went, and they also had me to their house on Christmas Eve after we had gone to Midnight Mass. They have been so wonderful to me and helped to keep my spirits up all along since I have been alone. We all are growing older. They, I guess, cannot see Bill. But, he, too, has been good to me, teaching me to drive, understanding from his own loss, helping with the house, and in just being a man. I appreciate what I have and do the best I can. I guess I am more humble. Bill and I met his sister at the plane as she came home from her daughter's in Texas last Sunday.

Your sisters are all nice to me. Mamie is in Arizona for four months, Nellie asked me over the phone to fix her taxes again, and Minnie, poor Minnie. But she works, she keeps cheerful, the dairy is gone, Woodie is fighting the fight against cancer. Shirley sent pictures of Minnie's four grandchildren and a nice letter Christmas.

The taxes are done and I did Florence's too. On Tuesday I checked poetry for Mr. Baldus and his wife. Do you remember him? The house needs many things, but I haven't been staying home much. But, oh, how much farther I am than last year at this time!

Then the car was worrying me, and it still does in bad weather. I backed it halfway out of the garage Thursday and decided to let it run about twenty minutes. As I turned to anchor the garage door, the car went rolling across the road and into the next yard. I raced to it, swung the door open, and stepped on the brake before it hit anything, or was hit. I thought of the riderless horse in funeral ceremonies of state.

Yes, ex-president Johnson's funeral was, and Truman's, and Nixon is the only living president. I watched Nixon's inauguration recently.

TV helps, church helps, clubs help, walking helps, shopping helps, neighbors help, relatives help, nature helps, and time pulls one along. I keep many things in my heart, and I ponder upon the meaning of it all. I sometimes wonder if you chose to live no longer, if God whispered to you that your time was nearly up, or if just plain chance took you from me. There are so many strange things in connection with our separation and the timing was so unusual. Things I did not think of at first, or for a long time, have emerged from somewhere, and I wonder—when I should accept.

January, the month of beginnings, is almost over. Perhaps as January ends, my writing to you may end. Perhaps I have gone through the stages of widowhood and perhaps there is not too much to say. You are a part of me, in my heart and mind forever.

In London I saw a play, *I and Albert,* about Queen Victoria, and her loss touched Elizabeth and me deeply. One line was "Oh, Albert, I would never have died and left you." And how she lamented afterward for ever so many years! That you would not have me do, nor would I have wanted you to do. It is very different—living it—from talking about it as we did sometimes. The pictures on the walls, the books in the cases, the dishes in the cupboard, the lamps on the tables—all were much more precious when we both owned them and used them.

I remember how when we sometimes quarreled, you would say, "I can leave." And I never once said that to you, though perhaps I said much worse, but I would say, "Well, it's all right if you do leave me, but your plate will be on the table every meal even if you aren't here. So come back, anytime." And you never left, not then.

But there came a time when you really left and could never return. But you left me so much, including the scent and sight of your beautiful roses; and now I leave you, praying that the future of my life is worthy of red roses at the end—and that I run to you, reaching out for me, through the valley of the shadow, when my turn comes.

April 2, 1973

Harry, the trees are budding, the grass and the hedge are greening, now and then a blue jay or a cardinal pauses in the front yard. And I feel a renewal and a desire to put things in better order and cleanliness. There are things to do in this house even though it is not the haven or the home it once was. Do you remember when I had the apartment with the balcony and you would get ready to drive the twenty miles to Garrett, how we would hate to say good-by? It was almost impossible. We would kiss and I would cry and you would hold me tight, and we would hunger for the time when it would not be thus. And how wonderful it was when at last we could be together! Something like that pulls me back to this writing when I have already said good-by in January.

But it is April now—two years ago I had sewing club on that second day of this month. It was a happy party and we enjoyed the leavings after we took Ethel to Ossian. The next day you got that pain at the back of your neck and it hurt me so. Then in the evening paper we learned Agnes Paschen had died suddenly at their new lake home. And on Sunday we were not able to go to them because of your pain. You asked me to write because your arm would not let you—you didn't feel equal to driving a car either. Later your finger got jammed in a closing door at school. But days come and days go.

Honey, Joe Lillich died too, of congestive heart failure at thirty-four, on his way to his new job in Jersey City. He had always been so good to me. Venetta and Grace and I spent a lot of time with his folks. The people from Indianapolis came up one evening to the funeral home. I gave his mother my book, *Grief*, and we ate with his family after the funeral at their home.

Harry, I have just come back from two weeks in Mexico. We flew to Mexico City, then bussed to Vera Cruz, Merida, and all around the famous ruins which we climbed and examined. Then we flew to Oaxaca, then to Acapulco, then home where we could not land in Chicago because of stormy weather, but we finally went on to Detroit and back to Fort Wayne by Delta. The big DC-10 was luxurious from Acapulco. Marvoline was my roommate, and we talked a lot about you and Ed, and how it is without both of you. Two widows, older than their husbands. Mexico, especially Oaxaca, was beautiful and warm, from about seventy-five degrees to 105 once. There were gorgeous lilac-like trees, and lovely flowering red ones, and brilliant orange ones. There was a beautiful brick cottage named "Irene," surrounded by geraniums and lantana. There were hedges with carved animals in them. On March 18 we had to step carefully on icy steps and wade through snow banks in our lightest possible clothes, because in Mexico it was sleeveless dresses and summery attire. How strange to come back to rain and cold and winter clothes! Marvoline and Alice Nord and I, three recent widows, taxied home to lonely houses. But I called Florence, then Bill came at 9:00 p.m.

Yes, Bill came, bringing me some fried chicken he had fixed

for supper, but we went to Atz's for a cheesburger, a cherry sundae, and coffee that was out of this world, next to the Mexican pineapple. Last night he cooked a beef roast with potatoes and carrots, and had a tomato salad. With wine first, and coffee later, it was perfect. He likes the pictures of me taken in Mexico, and he says I am the best of the crowd. It sounded true to me, and I look happy and smiling, though heart aches come and go. And I remember telling one wife how horrible it is to be a widow. There were five couples, five widows, and one widower on the trip besides our leader, a thirty-ish bachelor.

Today I collected my mail and read and thought. Yesterday I unpacked and washed my clothes, the ones that were soiled from traveling. Tomorrow I must go to my deposit box, and also the banks for interest.

Honey, before I left, I went to my folks to say good-by, and Bill took me to your folks where he was well received. We also went to your parents' grave and to yours—Bill had already been to his wife's grave, and he called to take me to yours. Irvin Bandelier's wife, my eighth grade teacher, is very near you—it gave me a good feeling.

In Manila last summer, a Barbara Williams from Elwood, who works in the school superintendent's office, talked to me over a native drink and nuts about her widowhood and also about a Bob who had stepped in. Of course, I talked about you, and about having Bill. Today I had a letter from her—she is marrying Bob on April 20. She is younger than I, but we have a lovely picture taken together at a night club in Bangkok. Florence told me today Bill would be awfully good to me, but I must be very sure. I do know life without him, now that you are not here, would be quite barren. So I will just try to do the best I can, and keep on with a long-time favorite quote: "Make you the world a bit more beautiful and better because you have been in it." Then there are the words of a song: "I would look up, and laugh, and love, and lift."

Goodnight, Harry, wherever you are—and help me if you can. Your love was the richest thing I had in life. I was so lucky to find you. We had so much in common. It is almost two years since the saddest time of my life, but there have been so many blessings and newnesses along the way that I cannot be bitter. I loved you, I loved teaching. I lost both in the merry month of May. Now I love life—or I guess I do—how wicked not to love, love, love.

April 3, 1973

Honey, I am right back again. This has been a cool, damp, gray day. Helen W. called about sewing club on Friday and we talked about Mexico. Florence came and so I missed the 10:05 bus, but got the 10:50 for downtown. I went to the deposit box for my jewelry and the bank books to collect the quarterly interest. It scares me—the money—there is so much of it. I must do the right thing—you worked so hard for it. I shall try to be wise, but oh, how I wish we could have managed it together.

At home, as soon as I picked up your twenty-fifth anniversary watch at Springer's, I fixed the garbage can and took stuff out—you always did that. The yard was full of papers and I picked up the biggest ones. There is so much to be done—sticks, stones, dead flowers from last summer. The roses are leafing out, the ones that are still alive. You would be putting on fertilizer and perhaps even mowing.

In the house as I watched television, I noted the salt and pepper shakers during the commercials. Side by side, they were reminders of the fact that all we owned was very dear when the two of us were together. At coffee time the two roses inside the cup winked at me as I sipped.

In the bank today I met Opal S. who drove me to Columbia that first summer. She was losing her love, a doctor who met another girl in the hospital, I think. Her sorrow came early, no married love, just a college teacher, retiring this year.

Lucile called to welcome me back from Mexico. She and Walter are having a quiet spring vacation week. She stays home with him more now—is not going to Women's Club Thursday or to sewing club Friday.

I opened the garage and looked around. The car you bought is like new. I love it and I want to drive it more skillfully. There are changes I must make in the garage, things I still must find out about. This will be the third summer, and I think now I will just stay at home and pull things together better than I have been able to do.

The house was decorated in 1964 and it will be ten years in 1974, next year. Of course, your heart attack was in November, and we couldn't finish until 1965, but we got it done. It was so pretty and so comfortable, and I wanted just to keep house while you taught. Of course we had our summers—glorious summers—but

117

Father took up much of our time then, though you never seemed to mind. So I just have to do things to the house now.

I thought about Bill and marriage. He has lived since 1927 in his house, and it must be all he wants, with his dog, Susie. And would I be happy with him all the time, here or there? Perhaps it is best as a "see him when you want" thing. I am a man's woman, and I can think of no one who would appeal to me more—after you. Often I am lonely, and sort of frantic, but I try to quickly conquer it. I am so rich in health, in wealth, in relatives and friends, in knowledge, in spirit, I think. I have fought against futility, and I must hope through to what futurity God gives me. They say I have done well, they have said it from the first.

When you met me on the banks of the Hudson in 1939, you liked my quick answer to, "Are you tired from your long ride?" "Oh, no, not at all, not one bit," and my eyes sparkled at being in New York again, and at meeting you. With that same liveliness of spirit and that same sparkle, may I go forth—to whatever else there is. And I know, "Mr. Kalabash," wherever you are, you will love me for it.

"The Lord bless you and keep you. The Lord make His face to shine upon you, and be gracious unto you. The Lord lift up his countenance upon you, and give you peace."

So, in my peace, as Eugene O'neil says in *Long Day's Journey into Night,* maybe it is as in Mary's speech: "The past is the present, isn't it? It's the future, too. We all try to lie out of that, but life won't let us."

June 11, 1973

Honey, it is nine o'clock and I have just spent the evening in the yard watering the roses and setting out the last of the little flowers to gladden our home. It was ninety-one degrees today, so it was not cool, even in the evening. But I enjoyed doing the work you did and thought of you almost overpoweringly.

Your roses are lovely, some of them. I took two pictures of them this morning with the new camera I bought in April. I worked in your old hobby jeans. The orange blossom bushes are at their best. The moss roses are coming, but I am not having snapdragons any more—too much like weeds. I am going to keep everything as nice as I can. Wouldn't it be fun to do it together? And that reminds me, the windows haven't been washed since you left. And

118

the car needs a bath too. Oh, honey—well, this week is pretty clear, so I may get a lot done.

Two years ago tonight, I was retired. Today I went with Lucile to the Retired Teacher's meeting from 12:30 to 3:30. I saw one woman with white hair who had very black hair when I last saw her. I saw balding heads and bulges over belts, and women with odder shapes than formerly. Some hands trembled, some steps faltered, and so many I remembered as they were in the thirties and on. Some people don't have to grow old, they go yonder with glow of youth.

I felt young and pretty in my rose and white outfit with a rose bracelet from Vienna and a cameo ring from Rome. Your wedding band and the twenty-fifth anniversary watch made me proud and happy. Some women never make it. Oh, how grateful I am for you and all we meant to each other.

Harry, in August I am going to Scandinavia, Scotland, and Ireland. I am rooming with Frieda Guilford who was in Europe with our group in '71 and in Asia with us in '72. It is good to have something to look forward to, something exciting. Venetta is finishing her master's and nursing four days a week at the Lutheran.

Walter and Lucile had a birthday party Friday night at their house. Just Grace made six of us with Marcia and Terry. We took pictures with my camera and had a delicious dinner. I think Walter is teaching just one more year. I drove after night—it is different with all the lights everywhere.

Saturday I went to your grave alone and washed the bird-visits and kicked the grass away from our marker. I wasn't satisfied with the grass but the nearby tree is lovely, and the Bandelier and Harding stones are comforting. I remembered standing on the little hill with the May wind in my hair and trying to decide if this would be the right place for us. Many things, too many almost, became my job suddenly.

The television, the air conditioner, the broken window, the redecorating, oh, there is so much to see about. "This one thing I do," one thing at a time, and one lives on awhile. I must get as much joy as I can as I go on.

Yesterday I drove to church feeling almost giddy with freedom from detail in driving. It may come naturally. I stopped in the chapel alone and put my hand on the back of your chosen pew

119

and drank in all the blue and red and white beauty before I went on into the sanctuary.

How I wish I could have another chance with you in some ways! I think I am so much wiser about so many things. Love is the most precious thing in the world—the love of man for maid. You were so dear an so many ways. You were so sensitive and you had so much to bear. Was I good enough? I know I was sometimes, but for some times I should be very sorry, I fear. Or is that daily living strain? Anyway, for every hurt you had, I hurt—even now. I loved you so! And you, I know you loved me. Oh, to clasp each other again! As we did so many times!

This man-woman situation—this fulfillment thing. How do people live without it? I know. I know. Yesterday Bill came to take me to his house for supper at four. He has understood me better than anyone. We talked of you and of Esther, and we go along together helping each other and being the closest of friends. He fixed steaks for supper and afterward we sat on his patio with his dog, Susie. The roses were vibrant and the cross on the church was golden in a completely blue sky. After a glass of wine each, he picked a huge bonquet and we came here. You are in my heart and Esther is in his, but we clasp each other because we understand and because we are alive. It is a facet of my life that appeared when it was needed and that seemed right. But I doubt if marriage would be right. How wonderful if it could be! How truly wonderful! Marriage is the ideal way of life for two who can have what we had, our books, our beliefs, our similar backgrounds.

Honey, your sisters all sent me birthday cards and notes. Nellie made me a string of jet beads. Did I tell you Venetta and I stopped at Platner's for supper a while back and visited your sisters, Nellie and Minnie? We were also at Ayres' and talked to Mamie and Mike.

Oh, there's so much to tell—so much goes on all the time. And I feel this great gush of wanting to share it with you. And there are the lonely times when I reach out for you in thought and emotion. That is the way it is. At church one Sunday during the coffee hour I sat alone. Others came to join me, but I will not intrude. I looked at a table where Cleon and Ruth sat with friends, and I thought, "It is bitter brew a widow drinks." Yes. really, although I say thank-you to God many, many times for the riches

120

I have had and still keep having.

After all, we were together in your dying, your hand pressures told me what you could not say in words—not every one is that lucky. And after all, without you, my dear, there have been—well, here I am at a loss for there is such a strange stoppage. Most things are better shared with one's true love. Far countries, many friends, pretty clothes, money, you-name-it, they all pale when compared with a togetherness blessed at the altar of God.

I am a widow. I was always, even when very young, fearful of being a widow sometime. Now my fears have come upon me. I have lived through two years of it. I am starting the third year. I may stay a widow. But I can live a good day every day, I hope. I will try sincerely to be of good cheer. I will try to keep my affairs in divine order. I will cry only on God's shoulder. I will go forth in courage and listen for divine inspiration. I will not flaunt you or my woes. Though I will think of you often, I will face reality and act accordingly.

Oh, honey, there was an announcement in the paper this morning about two teachers in your school system being named outstanding teachers in America for 1973. And you were chosen from your system in 1971, but the letter announcing your award came posthumously. Did I ever tell you that?

So, you were a success in the two things every man needs most, in your work and in your love. I think you realized it. Then there were the U.S.A. trips, your church, and your flowers, especially the roses.

September 7, 1973

Oh, Harry, another school year is beginning, the year you would have to decide whether to go on one more year after this or to retire. September, for us, has meant school, a beginning. It means sewing club for me tonight at Lucile's. Helen Hartley will be up from Muncie—Dave will be away a year the 14th. It means social whirl—club life begins. And church, and Bill.

Honey, I worked so hard in the yard yesterday. You can imagine the shape it was in after six weeks of little attention. I used the last of the fertilizer in the big Ortho box and clipped bead blooms and pulled weeds and watered. In fact I am watering now with the hose out back. And I washed out the garbage cans. There is yet so much to do. Mr. Nahrwold mowed while I was away. I told him not to do too much, just to keep the grass looking like someone lived here because he has a job at the City-County Building. Must change the hose now.

I just sniffed a red, red rose as I came to the dinette table. Harry, it is so fragrant and so beautiful and it has such healthy green foliage. It is almost a message from you. I found it yesterday. It was hiding, and I found it after all the hard work—in the farthest corner of the yard. It was low on the back of the bush, but it has a nice stem and is resplendent as those you so often picked for me. I wish you could see it.

Some of the sadness and hurt that dotted my trials and my busy life is moving out, and in its place is a new kind of beauty and almost happiness. I am so grateful for you and your love that I say "Thank you, God" many, many times. And I gain strength and a sweet kind of peace. It is so strange.

Our Decatur High School class reunion was June 17, a great success with everyone happy seemingly. Florence and I went together. There was a group picture taken in color. You would be proud of both of us. Florence means so much to me, and it is so nice to have her just six blocks away. She called just now to check on me before she goes to the Lutheran Home to play the organ for vespers. Ken works at the Lutheran Hospital on Fridays between ten and three. I haven't volunteered for anything yet to make the world a better place.

When I was outside a moment ago, a teen-age Negro boy and his two companions came next-door. The pretty mama left her teen-age daughters and went away in the car. Like everyone else around, I sometimes worry about the way the neighborhood is changing, and about how much to put in toward making our home prettier. Two women in the city have been murdered in twenty-four hours, one a thirty-five-year-old lady who had been to a church meeting, killed in the yard of her home; the other, an eighty-five-year-old lady was raped and killed in her bed. There have been several misdemeanors by blacks recently.

Oh, I forgot to say when talking about our high school class that three have died since June. Russel Smith, son of our small town doctor, was beaten to death in a parking lot; Bernard Clark had a heart attack; Dr. Gerald Kohne, who had had previous heart attacks, also had the last one. I guess we are a part of the passing generation.

Oh, yes, I went to Norway and Sweden and Denmark and Scotland and Ireland on August 1. I can't begin to tell you how wonderful it was and how rich it made me feel. Roomed with Frieda Guilford, and we were often with Mildred Louthan of Angola and her sister, Catherine Hostettler of Elkart, we four being the only people from Indiana. And there was a nun and her lovely sister from Pennsylvania; the nun wore slacks and a wig. For evening at dinner she wore a long dress and dangling earrings. How different! She taught first grade in a public school as Miss Murphy till 4:00 and until the next morning she was Sister Rosemary. The roses and flower gardens were so beautiful in those countries—perhaps because of cooler weather, longer days, and more moisture. If you were here, I could tell you much more about the trip by degrees.

Oh, Glenn Magner died of a heart attack while driving in Swinney Park—his funeral was yesterday, but I couldn't make it. The last time I saw him was when he came to the funeral home to visit you. His mother is in her eighties—he was sixty-two, like you. Am glad his mother has a sister—at least I suppose that was the way it was.

All morning today I was doing business down town. Went to the Lincoln Life to try to decide what to do with our annuity fund. Next week they will mail me options and tell me enough so I can decide whether to take monthly payments over ten years, or to leave it as a bank account. Then I went to the Lincoln Bank to straighten out the hassl over $30,000 because I had put your name with "or" on two of my "own money" accounts. Since July and August the lawyer, Lebamoff's partner, has been working on it. I think it is all settled now after several trips to the bank, the assessor's office, and the lawyer, Mr. VerWiebe. I want to get everything in order and to make a will.

While I was at the Lincoln Life, a tall Negro with a Yule Brenner haircut, stopped to chat and remind me that I didn't come to the tenth class reunion. You remember Arthur Page? He was so delightful, the only student at Central High who was elected class president four years straight, and at a time when whites were in the majority. He was so kind always and so thoughtful. Is now a lawyer associated with Lincoln Life. You and I have so many people we have been with day-by-day in schoolrooms. What a joy to see them accomplish and to have them accord you the respect they portray! What a grand teaching life we had! Of course there were challenges, but we weathered them together.

Helen Burr phoned. She is bringing your *Children's Literature* back and also a bag of wilted lettuce tomorrow. I have good neighbors. Mrs. Nahrwold talked a half-hour while I was working in the yard yesterday. Mrs. Wichern also stopped to talk when Harold and she came home. Mrs. Murphy and Mrs. Haines came over when the monkey came down out of the tree you bound up and saved after a car wreck flattened it out. I was sweeping the walk out front when what should have been a squirrel came down headfirst out of the tree and hurried across the street to the low pines and to the porch eaves and then on to the top of the house where it could laugh at the barking neighborhood dogs. Finally it gave them the slip and scurried south with the safety of some fences.

Sometimes I think I keep getting wiser all the time. I read so much and there is more time to think. I wish I knew as much ten years ago as I know about sex now from reading, from observation, from talking to people, and from feeling.

Ethel just phoned and she talked and then she talked again. Trivialities. How I hope I never get too talkative like some women I know. To you, I could talk a lifetime, but then maybe I have already done it and am starting over again in this somewhat peculiar way. Oh, Harry, there is so much I could "be with you" about. I could tell you about little Renee who is now troubled. You used to tease her about the "fairy people" in your yard. And she saw them too.

Venetta chose a beautiful apartment to furnish. Bill Hart invited her and Grace and me to his Debbie's wedding. Maybe it is all trivial talk, but with you, even me alone, life is so everlastingly great. Is there more? You know—I have yet to cross the bar.

September 23, 1973

Here I am, honey, right back again, and I feel a glow of happiness, maybe because I dressed in a colorful floral with black patent accessories and flaunted myself to church in the very new face of autumn which arrived at eleven-something last night. Cleon came to talk with me at the coffee hour about school and retiring in June. He and Ruth invited me to see their new carpet, after twenty-one years, and new linoleum because the sink flooded their home.

I came home, after a good sermon on being controversial, reminded me of you, like a cowboy riding in your sand and green Chevy of slightly over three-thousand miles. Where haven't I been? Fixed a good lone "chow" and watched out the scalloped awnings at the leaves falling from the locust tree. I would mow them up tomorrow, but Friday I put Winter Green on the grass, and I should wait for a shower, I suppose. Thus thinking, a pure white butterfly floated across the window expanse and it was almost a symbol. Yes, of you, strangely.

Falling leaves, and angel wings. Last Sunday, Florence and I went to Herbert Youse's funeral and sat with Jeanette. Irvin Bandelier was behind us. Then Florence and I went to her church to the senior citizen's group. Thoughts of Herbert kept coming. Bill came later in the day. Everything keeps me so busy, it seems. On Wednesday evening I went to the funeral home for Doris Coblenz who was with Marvoline and me in Mexico and also at the Women's Club. I told her husband I knew how it was and how it would be. He is such a young looking sixty-five. Is it a sin to wish I could know him better? In Mexico I enjoyed the both of them so very much.

That same morning Bill took me to the dentist for another gold tooth, the second one in six months. And just last night Bill joked as he sat down to supper with me, "Where's my bib, honey?" mocking his sister's boyfriend Alvie. Later, about 8:00 a call came from Defiance saying that Alvie had died of a heart attack two hours earlier. Strange, how we talked of Bill's sister and Alvie during that interim. Falling leaves, fading persons.

I must try to get more work and more thinking done, and quit butterflying. Did get three windows washed last week, and naturally I thought of you, because you last did them—with a little bit of help from me. And as I was on a ladder in the garage rummaging about the fertilizer and plant foods stored above in the open attic of the garage, I found a cache with some cigarette lighters, two cans of lighter fluid, and a bottle of Scope. Honey, I must really have driven your habit underground. Maybe there's a bit of my mother's mother in me. It seems grandmother might have sent grandfather drinking and to an early death by being too strict about a "nip" and a deck of cards.

As I see it, there was really nothing ever between us but my wanting you not to smoke because of health reasons and yes, the filth and smell they made in the house. And how sad I was when

I found the tipped grate in the basement and a half-smoked cigarette under it where you probably put it when you fell before you called to me for help. As Venetta says, "It is so hard for some people to give them up." But oh, what woes did you try to cover with a smoke screen? Sometimes we wish we could go back to a second chance, to do better by those we love. But we can only go forward.

Bill is fixing a pork loin roast tonight, and he will probably do it outside as the weather is ideal. He will have talked on the phone to his sister. We went to his wife's grave last week after I got my new gold tooth and then to your grave. We fixed a meat loaf dinner at my house afterward, and he sawed a projecting limb off the locust tree.

Not long ago we worked so hard trimming the hedge and mowing the yard and pulling weeds and trimming bushes. We both took showers—he brought his clean clothes in a brown sack. Then we drove to get chicken and fat sugar cookies on Lafayette Street. I had made potato salad. When we came back at dusk, we were locked out. I had forgotten my keys, so I tried at Nahrwold's to get a locksmith on Friday night to no avail. Bill sat in the car and ate a chicken leg. And well enough, for he had finally to get Helen's ladder and climb in the upstairs window to the south to get in the attic, and then drop down to unlock the back doors. No supper ever tasted so good when we finally got to it, and he brought in from the trunk of his car a new kind of grape wine. Ah me, the comfort of the inside of a house, and the feel of a good meal, and the homeyness of a good companion. Life, I now know so well, must be a shared adventure, else it is very, very sour vinegar.

Swinging into sweetness, before I leave you, I hasten to say that of all the best of my life, you were the 'bestest.' I know you corrected me for speaking often in superlatives where comparisons were better, but Harry, that is the way it was. And that superlative comes through, very clearly, you for me, and I for you, in so much of our glorious existence together. You are the only person I ever felt absolutely, completely, "at home" with.

November 4, 1973

Harry, I have just come in from the out-of-doors where I went to gaze at the red and yellow maple you saved so long ago. It is as pretty as the one we liked halfway down the block on the other side of the street. The locust is a skeleton, but oh, you red maple! I fairly itched to clean up the locust sticks but it is Sunday, and I don't want to get sweaty even if it is in the forties. There is a rosebud on the bush in the circular bed, but snow is forecast for tomorrow. And the awnings are still up. I know how you would enjoy taking care of your part-acre, for I have learned your love of nature and the joy of working with hands.

We had such a beautiful blue-skied October, and I got through our wedding anniversary for the third time alone. I drove to New Haven about the car, but on the way I stopped at your place. The cemetery entrance was beautiful with gay colored leaves. I got out of the car and walked to your rose-colored stone, and many precious thoughts came to me, grateful thoughts for our life together, and thankfulness for the mantle of courage that seems to emanate from you, even in death. The essence of true happiness for me would be to run into your arms and hear you say, "I love you," as you said it so often. To have you hold me tight and tenderly. Since that can never be, I shall remember a definition of happiness I read recently from Dr. Murray Banks: "Happiness is not a destination, it is a manner of traveling."

After the car was checked, I drove out to Marilyn's but she wasn't home, so I went to Shirley's. It was her wedding day too, and we talked while she rested from cleaning her car. Then I went to Lloyd's and he took me for a ride to Ossian through the autumn colors, past Aunt Etta's house which is being remodeled, and to the bakery where we bought cookies and donuts. On the way back we stopped for sandwiches at Poe, huge breaded veal tenderloins on sweet buns. Lloyd and I talked of you and of Gerry. He is on the cemetery committee at Hoagland, and he took me to see what had been cleaned up and the changes that had been made. Of course we saw Gerry's grave and my parents' and ever so many more. Then there were the new raw-earth graves of Ervin Koeneman, Herbert, Russel Smith, and "Frank" Houk. Life fountains for a time, and then the splashing ceases.

Bill came in the evening for supper. I cooked the banana squash we had got near the Michigan line two days before. It was luscious. My, what a day we had in the Pigeon River area that was so gorgeous with autumn! And what a delicious smorgasbord to end our day as we came back from our five-hour jaunt! We do have

127

good times together, but would we be happy if it were an all-time thing?

You remember the gray-haired widow who used to come alone to the eight o'clock service at church, then later she started bringing a gray-haired man? As I was coming from the parking lot to the church today, I passed them, and both spoke to me. They were so well-dressed, and their silver halos were glory above their shining pink faces. Truly they walked in radiance. I turned after I got across the street and waited for the light to change, but I peeked at them getting ready to ride away in their blue car. I walked on wondering if Bill and I could have that; and if so, what are we waiting for?

It is after 3:30 now. The house is in order. I have read in *McCall's* and in *Good Housekeeping* what Jacqueline Kennedy said about her husband on the tenth anniversary of his death. You and I were at the Stage Door restaurant that night and watched excerpts of what happened on TV. And you had to face heart attack and stroke. Oh, dear, how good we do not know our fortune ahead! Bill just phoned—he is coming early and we are to take the awnings down before the coming snow.

January 12, 1974

Oh, Honey, Honey, it is deep winter now and a new year too. Heaps of snow are everywhere, the steps and streets are icy. You would have had two free days, Thursday and Friday. It will go well below zero tonight, if it is one below at 8:00 p.m.

The snow began the 19th of December, big damp flakes that clogged the passage ways. I had a big sack of silky golden balls Bill had loaned me to decorate for the Retired Teachers' party, and I had gone to the Plymouth Church by bus, walking the last two blocks with high boots. As I walked into the church, I thrilled at the holly bush by the church steps, then remembering my deed, I rushed in and off the carpet to a tile floor—which came up and hit me as I tried to push it away. Result, a very painful right wrist and a left shaft of my glasses bent out of shape. I got babied a lot, stayed for the program and refreshments, let the others on my committee decorate, and then made the Lutheran Hospital as best I could in Marvoline's Pontiac. Not a break, a bruise and a sprain, and it was real rough learning to be a southpaw around the house. It was awful driving home from the hospital, wondering if we would make it, and I was so happy to know Marvoline made it home after she stopped in the middle of the street and let me burrow to the house through the deep whiteness.

I didn't have to wear the bandage to Danny's house on Christmas Day. My hair was freshly done, and I wore the green dress I bought in New Haven with red shoes and gold jewelry. Oh. Harry, it was wonderful to be with your people again on Christmas—all there except Shirley's family and Nellie's.

Danny and Woodice are both teaching at Tri-State College. Torbin was a year old Dec. 26. They get up at five, all three go to Angola before eight, and Tor goes to the babysitter while the parents teach. They are in the early thirties, I think, and they can so much fruit, and do so much toward finishing their two-year-old house. Woodice made all the drapes. Their year in Louisiana must have inspired them because the house is a big colonial on a twenty-acre lot. There are five bedrooms and two baths up, and down there are five rooms and a huge attached garage, and, of course, another bath.

The fireplace end is bricked to the ceiling, the silver is heavy and ornate; the master bedroom even has a fireplace, the bed a canopy that Woodice made. One of the upstairs rooms is her sewing room, another is a study.

Your nephew and wife, Steve and Linda, picked me up and I enjoyed Eric and Jamie on the way. They will have another in March. Jamie has dimples, angel kisses, his mother calls them, and he makes me think of you when he smiles, which is much of the time. He enjoyed the big Irish setter and the two smaller dogs. They both enjoyed everything, the huge tree and the dozens and dozens of colorful wrapped gifts. Somehow it seemed as if my presents were the nicest, perhaps a tribute to you.

I didn't take any because I didn't expect it to be so beautiful. I had given each of the nephews and nieces on your side fifty dollars, one-hundred on my side. Last year it was a hundred to yours, and fifty to mine. Now they are even. This money business is my job now, and it troubles me. A will should be made, and I am in the midst of taxes.

I forgot to mention the five pies Woodice baked and all the other goodies, even turkey and ham. And the picture taking. I have several good ones. Oh, honey, how I wish you could have enjoyed the yellow mansion as I did.

Bill and I had a Christmas with Florence and Ken with bridge afterward, and the day before Angola we had Christmas here. He gave me a floral robe, and I gave him brown leather slippers, house ones. We had New Year's Eve here with sauerkraut and pork loin and mashed potatoes. I made an apple pie that was delicious. Then New Year's Day he came at 11:00 for lunch and the Rose Parade and the game afterward. He went home at 8:30 because the temperature was dropping toward zero very fast.

I am definitely a man's woman, but I wonder if, as you always said I should, I will marry again. There was a card from John and a note—between the lines I know I could, but I wouldn't. Then Ralph answered the card I sent, a note included. This interests me, even more than Bill because he seems like you. He is college educated, blond, his wife taught twenty years, and he doesn't smoke or drink. He has been a successful person, but he lost a son, a daughter, and a wife in tragic circumstances. Now there is a granddaughter living with him while she studies radiology at the Lutheran.

These young people! I marvel at them as at Danny and Steve. And my niece, Sherry. She went to Berlin from Dec. 13 to Jan. 2, to visit Denny. Wanted me to go to be with her in the daytime, but I knew I shouldn't. It was such fun helping her get lined up at the travel service, and giving her my luggage and German marks, and going to the airport with Florence to see her leave and return. Those brown eyes with the long lashes! And a graduate nurse in May, with an offer from the Cleveland Clinic.

Harry, Mrs. Christman had breast surgery and goes back for ovaries out soon. Helen called and talked to me about it. And here I could go on and on about deaths and near deaths. Bill is busy cleaning out clutter, so am I. Today he sold his tools, such a big part of his life he said on the phone. His son wouldn't understand them, he himself had to do it though it hurt. I think about my books, and yours.

Oh, I am so thankful in so many ways about our life together. But if people would only realize how much they have while they have it. But they couldn't, the poignancy would be too much for living couples, that is the way I see it now. There were things I could have told you though, and why did I say some of the things that come back to haunt me? I like to think I could do better, if that were possible, and maybe you could—maybe we could look and really listen more.

Bill has a beef roast for tomorrow, weather permitting. Did I tell you how he roasted two chickens on the spit as he has done so often? Then he cuts one up for us to eat, and later he splits the other for us to have the next day. This time he called me to the table from the TV, and here was a whole chicken on my plate and a whole one on his plate. Both were on their backs, and he said over my amazement, "Eat why you want off it—take the rest home." So I did.

We have fun. At Thanksgiving he roasted a pork loin on the spit, and I have never seen a more luscious slice of meat coming my way. He made mashed potatoes and a lettuce-tomato salad. I had taken a pumpkin pie (a beauty) and whipped cream, also cranberry sauce. Of course there was wine and coffee and bread and butter.

Harry, the world is in such a sorry state. The Arabs won't sell oil to countries who favor Israel. It is crippling us and Europe, especially. There is constant talk of impeaching Nixon. I pay more taxes than he. It seems he has ways of evading them, and Agnew is in the same boat, only worse, he resigned. Inflation is terrific, crime is on the increase.

I just keep living a day at a time, trying to have a little fun, trying still to make the world a little more beautiful and better because I have been in it.

February 2, 1974

Sweetheart, I come often after an hour of evening news, a *Lawrence Welk Show*, and *All in the Family*. There is a white sifting over the outside, and I am alone. The family show had a boy like David in it, a retarded boy who was not so dumb, just the way you always talked about David. My heart goes out to people like that, and to their parents.

Being all alone here today, except for the half-hour Lucile and I worked on the Women's Club program, I thought of so many things. What to do about redecorating, what to do about the rest of my life, whether to expect a miracle of companionship again? Oh, there is so much to wonder about when the most valued person cannot help. I did get the house in order, but I really didn't clean, that means sweeping and dusting and scrubbing. To ease the thinking, I made a funny turnover pie out of some dough I found in the refrigerator. There was enough for the bottom of the pan, so I floured and sugared half of it. Then I put peach halves on that half with butter and lemon and cinnamon. Then over that I added more sugar and flour before I pulled up the bare sheet over the peaches and tucked it in under the far edge. Then I made a few slits for steam to escape while it baked for forty minutes. In forty more minutes after Lucile left at three, I made a cup of coffee and ate it. Never tasted a better pie, and my supper was pretty early. But it's a strange life alone.

Then I went back to my current book, *Portrait of a Marriage*, by Vita Sackville-West's son. It, too, is very strange, but interesting. How wonderful a life like ours was, and how I would like to live it over with the greater wisdom I now think I have! Naive, perhaps, but rich and expressive, even with tremors and earthquakes. Shared silences were even wonderful.

A year ago today was Joe's funeral, Dr. Lillich, if you please. Oh, Harry, he made my life so exciting for four summers with all those trips to Europe and Asia. And because of his introducing me to Elizabeth, I had Mexico, and the three women I went to Scandinavia with I met through Joe. Even Venetta came in more strongly because of Joe. She and I are attending a banquet at Baer Field Inn, Thursday. Last year was so full of change.

And in my heart there is a change that might come through, if God wills, a man very like you who sent a Christmas card-note and who had held my hands twice, once when his wife died and once on the street a week ago. I could be so proud of him and I think so in tune, but am I Cinderella and did he find my slipper at the fantasy ball?

Honey, I look out on the blue house halfway down the Baxter block west, and I see a young Negro man who bought one of the three houses for sale. This has been such a small townish neighborhood, but I wonder how long it will stay together. There are seven other Negro homes, not all a block away. We decorated in 1964. I wonder how much I should do again, alone and at my age, which doesn't seem so young, sometimes.

Nellie wrote that Mamie is in the hospital, she thinks for nerves. Did I tell you she fell at home and broke her right arm just below the shoulder the day after Christmas? You remember the auto wreck and how long it took her to get back the use of her left arm. Florence and I sent cards she should have by now.

Florence and I have done the taxes after many phone calls and a day of work here. Lloyd called twice yesterday and once today.

Eileen has a new job overseeing the delicatessan at Kroger's, Carol is hostess at a new restaurant, Peter's, and Jon has a new girl who is dietician at a nursing home. He's twenty-six and she is twenty-five, so it may be permanent. Lloyd has ordered a Masonic ring made with Gerry's diamond, and he is interested in a doctor's widow, it seems.

I found an interesting quote in a Joyce Brothers article in *Good Housekeeping* today. "Psychologists use the term grief work to describe the mourning process all human beings must go through before they can accept and adjust to a loss." You and I did so much homework as teachers and so much housework as married workers and it was such fun, really. Bill's helped me most, I suppose, with my grief work because he's lost his lovely wife. But then Lloyd helped me, and oh, I've been so blessed because so many helped, like Florence and Venetta. Lucile and Walter helped too. Did you remind God to remind them and all the others to help me?

Oh, I pray that I can be the woman God wants me to be, and the woman you would be proud of. I do not like the word resigned and I hate the word widow. So I must get on with life. Your doctor said last Monday I was all O.K. and that all he could give me was reassurance. He also added that I should take another trip. However, I feel I should get some things lined up so I don't trip over anything here, before I trip elsewhere.

February 13, 1974

Sweetheart, tomorrow is Valentine's Day—and I haven't got down the package of Christmas cards from a drawer in the attic to look lovingly at each and to read the bit of verse and pause in memory of each Christmas as I did for years even when you were here and with me. It was always such a very dear thing to do.

And I have lived almost three years without hearing "I love you" as only you could say it. How rapturous it would be to hear those words and bask in the enfoldment of your warm arms and nestle into your neck before reaching up for your kiss. As the song "Love Me Tender," you were the best that ever happened to me.

It is strange how wise I feel now that I have time to think, that I have talked to many people in strange lands, that I have had to learn how to do so much alone, that I have read so much, that

I have known Bill so well. I only wish I had had all that wisdom when you and I both could have profited from it. As it is, I shall have to use it day by day, not hoard it for an uncertain future.

Today I put the house papers together, the car papers likewise, then I fixed a leather folder for your last papers and one for my papers (for whom?), and made a folio of my insurance papers, our pension information, the Social Security records, checked the bank books, and my black book of financial affairs since 1932.

I discovered, though I have a binder, that the insurance policy for the car had not been sent. Tomorrow I must phone Washington, D.C., because it was promised in 4 weeks after the binder date of December 19. I drove the car to the laundromat and grocery over a snow bank and on wet and icy streets for the first time. I love the car you chose.

Marvoline has had painting and fixing done, and that is what I must do here, though how much worries me some. I would feel so strange in a new house though this neighborhood is changing. Monday I went to a committee meeting in Grace Lloyd's new apartment in Canterbury Green. It was lovely, but I feel I want grass and flowers and a garage. My greater wisdom will have to work this out. Linda told me on the phone that Mamie is worse over her broken arm than after the wreck. The doctor said she had never had trouble all her life and she didn't know how to take it. I hope she mends mentally and otherwise. There are those who think Mike isn't much help. Marie wrote me that Kirk may be getting married this summer—he is eighteen this month.

Lloyd phoned me this week that little Jon is getting married on our parent's wedding day, March 16. Later Jon called me to say he was honeymooning in Georgia. Jon's girl graduated from Purdue in home economics and now is a dietician at Lawton Nursing Home. It is good they both have college degrees and that they are twenty-six and twenty-five. They were going to have a simple wedding, but her mother is planning otherwise.

Honey, Bill is coming tomorrow night. I am cooking a roast with potatoes, onions, and carrots—Valentine cookies and ice cream for dessert. There's red currant wine and coffee, of course. But, honey, this is awful, I hope the man "like you" stops to talk to me as I go to the Women's Club tomorrow at ten. There have been three close contacts that have set bells ringing in my heart.

134

March 10, 1974

Hi, Harry, it's 9:30 on a lonely Sunday night and I've been a sick shut-in for three days, but I'm getting better. It took me about a week to really come down with sore throat for three days, and then no breath and raining tears, nose blowing, and the rest of the flu line-up. I've been so miserable—it's horrid to be sick alone and fearful. Ken brought bread and cookies last night, Bill has called—but I wouldn't give this to my worst enemy.

And just when I had a little free time to clean house and plan things and do clothes. Jon's wedding is Saturday, a Women's Club bridge, lunch, and style show Thursday, Bill's birthday, Wednesday, Marilyn's shower on Tuesday. Then Vera, Lenora Hanes and I have to be hostesses for the Sunday meeting of the Truth Seekers from 3:00 to 6:00.

I got up at 8:00, read the Sunday paper, rested, thought about the man "like you" who set bells ringing in my heart at last writing. Honey, I met him Thursday again on my way to Women's Club and we stopped to chat. If something comes of it, I might be awfully happy as you said you wanted me to be. Bill has been dear and wonderful to me, but we are not for marrying. Some women, I suppose, never forsake romance. A quotation from Kahlil Gibran comes to mind: "In marriage Love creates a happiness that no other happiness can surpass but that of the Soul when she embraces God." But could one love, really love again? Nevertheless, this solo way of life is still strange, but I've learned to swing it in spite of the sadness that is so engulfing at times.

In the afternoon I cooked some beef in the Dutch oven. I can still see my eighty-year-old father carring it into the dining room from the kitchen when he wanted me to take it. I rested some more, watched *Knights of the Round Table* beautifully done, and ate supper by candle light. Black people went by, showing through the narrow curtain openings. Life is so different. With you I wouldn't have hesitated to have the drapes wide open.

Lenora and I have the Sunday Truth Seeker supper bit planned after several phone calls—Easter theme, forsythia, green and yellow candles, colored candy eggs. The dishes are now done, and the news soon starts.

You would be sixty-five now. I stood by your pew in the chapel last Sunday and watched you escort people to seats and take up the collection, along with your handsome partner. The crocuses are out. On the fifth of this month I went out and found three yellow and two blue ones, so fresh and brave. And there are so many more to come. The tulips, too, are taller. John Moss, on TV, says it will get colder and rain tomorrow afternoon and evening. So I will be stuck in to nurse my cold and idle around some more, I suppose.

This agony and loss, this eating alone, sleeping alone, coming home to an empty house, never hearing "I love you," this being responsible for everything is bearable when one remembers the ecstasy of being together and for each other, when one remembers the constant movement of life and death, when one plans and searches for the miracles, small though they may be, in the present and future life. So much happens that is good and joyful and I have to be ready to see it.

Venetta just phoned and we had a long talk. Friends are wonderful, and how much Venetta and I have done in friendship—in churches and shrines in many cities, in planes high above the seas and mountains and plains, in groups of new friends here and there, in talks of life and love. With your blessing and your lovely sweetness in memory I press on miracleward.

March 19, 1974

Harry, I've just been out in the yard about half an hour picking up sticks, litter, and pinching off some of the roses and plants with snippers. Honey, the roses have red bumps where new shoots are coming out, and it's srping in two days even if the temperature is only thirty-seven, no breezes. I see how much work is to be done to make our place pretty, and you must have loved it.

Yesterday I bought a book, *I Married a Farmer*, by Delight Bobilya (Wier) and she says, "The happiest people in the world are flower lovers." She says so many delightful things, and there are lovely family pictures in this book. One of the many joys of teaching is in learning what former pupils do with their lives. I remember her in my fifth grade class, and also in the sixth. How enthusiastic and bubbly she was! I see in her writings the love and joy and work of my parents on the farm, and the knowledge and wisdom we three children gained from the growing plants, the animals, and the skies all four seasons. The few hills, the open ditch, the woods—so much to explore. And how great to be sent to the basement with its bins of apples and potatoes, its glass jars of cherries, peaches, pickles, colors of a cathedral window.

Also yesterday I went to the library where I found a book the newspaper doctor recommended for heart patients, *Sex after Sixty*, by Rubin. I must have found the wrong Rubin for the first name was different and the title was *Active Sex after Sixty*. I wonder if I know what inactive sex is. Anyway I read all I wanted and then went to the Rachel Circle at the church. Is inactive sex what drabs so many faces and lessens zest? I paid my dues and decided not to belong another year. And then I thought of people like Catherine the Great, in the book, and Lady Churchill and other weird or wild or zestful people. If the by-products of a happy life together are serenity and poise and charm, why don't more people realize what they have or can have? Is it luck, or desire, or imagination, or subtlety, or God's gift?

Anyway, I wish you and I had talked more that last year about all there is to talk about. So many things seem unsaid now and so many understandings seem lost. I thought we were happy, that we were secure, that the summer would be a time to have a bit of heaven on earth, but alas, our summer was not, not ever again.

Bill and I went with Florence and Ken to Jon's wedding in Saratoga—such a lovely bride and groom. They are in Atlanta this week and then home to take up life's burdens along with the pressures of joy. Florence insisted Ken's eyes were better for night driving, and so we got home after eating a late supper in Berne with Marilyn, Ray, and Amy. Yesterday Ken got his car wrecked as he was parking at Southgate. A woman hit him broadside. So much can happen in an instant. The repair bill will be nearly a thousand dollars.

I filled the car with gas yesterday, nearly sixty cents a gallon. I love the car and hope I can drive more this year. The world is in a sorry state, Arabs sitting on oil, several kidnappings for huge ransoms, public officials resigning, people laid off in auto industries, talk of impeaching a president who will not give up, inflation.

I modeled an African dress for Ruth Fleck's "Vistas of Kenya" tonight at A.A.U.W. A year ago I was in Mexico City—was reminded by lovely pictures of Dr. Frobenius at St. Luke's Sunday. Was hostess for the afternoon meeting of some senior citizens. Decorated tables with forsythia, pussy willows, green and yellow candles, crepe paper, and Easter eggs. Oh, I keep going, and it bothers me some that I don't have a trip planned, but there have been plane crashes and hijackings.

Sometimes I pray thankful prayers, and fearful ones when I don't know which way to go. Right now I believe I have an answer to the Bill situation—my feelings are null and void. Toward you that never could have happened. I feel there may be something new for me, something you would approve more of. If not, I am just me, and if God is God, I will make it, even on my own.

There are new Fostoria glass candlesticks that arrived in the mail today. Also on the table is a new book that arrived today. Beauty and knowledge to share are twice as much, but I can look and learn alone if my lot is to be such, if the man I secretly admire admires me not. Togetherness is evanescent eventually. To have no illusions, not to dream is for me a kind of death.

April 24, 1974

Sweetheart, I came home at 4:30 from playing bridge at Alice's and wished I had someone to cook supper for. Yesterday I came home from a Retired Teacher's luncheon at 3:30 and called Bill. He was not well and resting in bed, but he and I finally got around to deciding on supper together. I fixed a Cornish hen in broth and cooked some noodles and some sweet potatoes. There was good Holland Dutch bread and a mixed fruit salad with fresh pineapple in it. A good white Spanish wine and a pot of coffee. It was such heaven to fix the table pretty with green candles on a gold cloth.

The living room is better after the tear-up necessary for painting. I had worked hard Monday putting up cleaned pictures and sweeping thoroughly and moving the furniture back. The kitchen and cellar-way and hall-way are done, too. Honey, I am just now doing what we had planned for that awful unbeknown summer of 1971 when we parted. I couldn't do it before. Now after Vienna and Geneva and Madrid, the Orient, Hawaii, Mexico, and Norway, and Scotland, and Ireland, I can settle and bring some of their beauty here. I drank in some more of the beauty of your chapel Sunday and I vowed with eyes upturned to the lovely blue and red window I would try to make this house and this yard as pretty as we would have done it together, if I can.

May 6, the painter is coming to do the three back rooms. I am going to put the bath back in gray, but a silvery light Irish mist. The study is not going to be lemon yellow, but a deeper marigold.

The bedroom is going to still be pink for roses or Japanese cherry blossoms. Oh, how I tremble to think of moving the books and clothes in the closets, especially my shoes that have gone tramping, tramping. But how lucky I am to be able to do it somehow! There are all the drapes and the windows and woodwork to wash. Finally, there is the carpet to be cleaned.

After tomorrow, the last Women's Club meeting except the May breakfast, I'll start to organize for the painting. Oh, and there's the front window to be put in by City Glass, Then there's the outside trim on the house and the garage to be done when Mr. Baughman comes back from "around the world." What a project! On June 22 I am leaving for a Caribbean cruise with Freida. That's my week's vacation this year.

Harry, I've been such a joiner for the first time in my life. I am now a Sigma Delta Pi, a member of two church groups, A.A.U.W., Women's Club, Retired Teachers, a bridge club, and what-have-you. Out of my loneliness I twist and turn and search, and I find surcease of the aching that could engulf and overwhelm, but it is only for a time. I have only small bright bits in exchange for the all-encompassing contentment that was mine in your arms and in your very presence. Something vast is missing, but I shall look closely for glowing spots in life's constant movement. Moreover, I shall make life glow where I can. You understand?

Monday I drove through the rain to New Haven for my car inspection, but forgot the registration and had to go back for it. I stopped at our "final destination," looked at the stone, thought through the tangle of death, and drove on. Picked up the laundry on the way back, got groceries and gas, and had the afternoon for homework.

The yard really needs mowing and fertilizing. The roses need trimming. The garbage is out for tomorrow's pick-up. But I'll get it done finally, your work and mine.

When we were both teaching, we didn't see how much was to be done, or the sharing made it less. Anyway, there was so much that was wonderful in our lives, ninety years of teaching, so many part-time jobs, traveling over the U.S., and the breakfasts that started the days, and the suppers that brought us together at nights.

June 17, 1974

Sweetheart, sweetheart, how I missed you over the Decoration Day time, the third anniversary of your leaving! But I worked very hard to drown my feelings much of the time. I washed windows and storm windows, mowed the yard, got flower beds ready for planting, put the inside of the house back together. And on June 1, the day of your funeral, I was out chopping weeds at 7:00 a.m. The painting and the cleaning were to have been our work that summer we both left teaching. In three years I got it done. I manage the car much better. I try to keep pretty and gad about. It hurts to live alone, but I must not complain.

Honey, your white suitcase with the blue lining is yawning at me. It will do for one more trip, to the Caribbean. Frieda and I leave for Hudson, Michigan, over night at her brother's home and then on to Detroit in her car for the airport, then to Miami.

Saturday I bought three new dresses, a long navy print for dinner in the evening, a blue voile cocktail dress, and a yellow print casual—the last an eye-opener. But when I tried them on for Bill last night, he went "gaga" over the long dress, with which I will carry his wife's beaded bag. Florence also saw them today and very much liked them. Have the right jewelry and shoes and should be very happy. But when I put it all together for Bill, I ached for you to see them. You liked clothes, and I'd like to wear them with you. How rich, how very rich we could feel!

Bill is dear and sweet, and I know he comes up feeling "a lacking," but what can I honestly do? I have been sitting here weighing the marriage I might have with the one I did have, and the scales won't balance. Could I accept the difference and face the world with him—as he would, I think, gladly accept me? Could I feel proud of him, as I did of you? Oh, I feel ashamed when I think how happy he would be. But I can't marry cigarette and beer and non-college. He's no dummy, but there's a type of class you had that he hasn't. Maybe I am contemptible—but no one really encourages me in regard to him. We do have our moments and we understand each other, and we've shared the same type of loss. It is good to have someone to cook for and to feel loved—but I wish I could feel unshakably right about someone. Guide me, O thou great Jehovah!

Honey, Dr. Meister is gone too, and she's teaching in New Jersey. I know how much he meant to you. In the springtime too, with cancer of the pancreas.

I read a new book, *Widow*, by Lynn Caine, and I returned it to Anna Thompson today. Anna was left after eleven years of marriage with three little children, her husband was killed in a train wreck. We talked of the book and of our experiences.

My birthday was celebrated here with Grace, Walt, Lucile, Marcia, and Terry. I served ham, scalloped potatoes, a new type of bean salad, and a jello square at the place. Pickles, olives, hot rolls. A cake with candles that Marcia provided, and orange ice cream or French vanilla. Nuts and candy that Venetta sent from the Dutch Mill.

The night before Venetta and Ethel took me to the Dutch Mill. Never will I forget the raisin pie with a pink candle in the ice cream that topped it. The evening after, Bill and I did my birthday. He gave me a Timex watch that I wanted. Florence and Ken came at noon the day after. I had made cookies for the Retired Teachers' party Monday before I went to church. Florence came, then I baked the cookies while Bill was here in the afternoon. Your sisters all sent me cards.

Honey, I've been very social—to Indianapolis to visit Hope, Welcome, and Phil on Wednesday. DeNeal and Grace along. Dinner at Ted and Tom's South on Thursday with Venetta, followed by a play at the Fine Arts, *The Lady of the House*. Steaks and salads at Bill's house on Friday, and to a party at Alice Martin's for the Lillichs on Saturday. The Lillichs are moving to Florida soon. Got home with Venetta at 2:00 a.m. after the after-party at the Lillich's. Monica and Tony made chi-chi's, a Hawaiian drink. Bill was here last night, and I couldn't sleep after he left. Finally, at 4:00 I added to the Valium I had already taken and slept till 8:00. Have had a fair day, though. To the laundromat, a sink wash here, began to organize for the trip. It has been dark all day and cold and now it's raining.

I forgot to tell you I had Sandpoint Greenhouse put out eight new roses. Some of them are blooming. The birthday bushes are beautiful. Need just a few plants yet and it's done.

And Mr. Baughman, dear man, did the outside of my house, then Nahrwold's, then at Marvoline's he fell and broke his leg. She was in bed at the time she heard the ladder fall, and she did what she could, called emergency at the Lutheran and called his best friend to get his car and supplies. He had just returned from a forty-day trip around the world when he came here. Mrs. N. and I enjoyed his singing while he painted and his music on the tape recorder. His pictures and his stories were interesting. But he didn't get along with Diane's dog, at all, at all.

I do hope I sleep tonight. Must do errands downtown tomorrow for the trip.

August 29, 1974

Harry, it is that time of year we looked forward to for so many years. Schooldays, and our particular niche for the next nine months, or so. And I've always treasured August, the last of leisure with the hint of excitement for a beginning with young people. This would be your last year of teaching.

So much has happened. The Caribbean trip was leisurely and lovely, blue waves on and on, the island scenery and shops, the entertainment on board, the dressing for dining and promenading, the people from everywhere. Freida's people were delightful, and her friends interesting. I liked the one man, Harlow Eastman, in our group, also his wife, a South Side graduate. A teaching friend of hers, and her friend completed our immediate group of six who were tabled together. And what food the good ship *Skyward*, a Norwegian vessel, served! From June 22nd to the 29th. Freida and I drove home from Detroit that last night by midnight. Freida is sixty-seven and is teaching another year.

I really needed the trip when I took it, after so much painting and cleaning and planting. Then when I came home I ordered new drapes for the two backrooms because the others got too holey in the cleaning process. They are lovely, pink and green in the bedroom, and yellow and green here in the study. Mrs. Nahrwold came over this afternoon, and Mrs. Wichern came this evening to see them. The latter has been giving me vine-ripened tomatoes. It is good to have longtime neighbors, but such strange new ones are coming in, all colors, and some seem really "characters." High boots, bare feet, purple pants, belly buttons, long hair, curly bushy heads, big hats, bill-backward caps. And so many bicycles with high orange flag warners. And you'd never believe the dogs. Some go to the bathroom in our yard.

The eight new roses are doing well, the yellow and orange marigolds, the zinnias and red salvia, the pink and white periwinkle, the orange and yellow lobellia, the violet browallia, the

142

geraniums, and moss roses.

I hear nice stories of you. Mrs. N. said one morning before they were up you planted little moss roses all along their garage because you had heard her say she liked them. She also said her husband, she thinks, feels your loss severely. Mr. Pettigrew came when I thought the roof leaked, and he said what the world needed was more men like you. He will fix the crack around the front steps and then I can do everything else to make this place as beautiful as possible inside and out. I mow the lawn like crazy when it isn't too dry for the grass to grow, and I drive the Nova down Clinton Street like a galloping bronco.

Tomorrow I go to a meeting of the social committee for Retired Teachers. Monday night I went out with Walt and Lucile to eat at Hall's across the Bluffton Road bridge. Met Mildred Meese and Helen Blackledge. Mildred had been with Marvoline in northern Europe. I was also with Walt and Lucile the previous Monday at a dinner for eight at their house, friends made on the first European trip. Then the Saturday before that I went with them to dinner at the K. of C. lodge where we had delicious roast beef, and an early happy hour with drinks at half-price. Walt is retired now, and he and Lucile may travel around the world on the *Queen Elizabeth* from January to March.

Venetta and I had a delightful day at Napanee the day Gerald Ford took the oath of office as president. Honey, Nixon resigned and there have been exciting political times. Well, Venetta and I breakfasted at her house before a lovely window at my right. TV excitement was at the other side, then when we had our new president we started out and had an Amish Fair day after a downtown furniture store and lunch. We looked at art work, drank cider, ate sausage and sauerkraut sandwiches in a big tent, watched a pig roasted and cut up, listened to an Appalachian ballad singer lady, bought scrapple and fudge and cheese, and "faired" real well. Saturday night last, we went to Zoli's from 8:30 to 10:30 and had Hungarian fare and wine sipping.

We were at Grace Lloyd's apartment for a final party for the Lillichs who are now in Kissimmee, Florida. I go to so many places. I feel so unsettled really, a bit like a bird with a broken wing. It takes two, you know, to really fly, and we lived in high, or so I thought. Much of our life was like *Jonathan L. Seagull* by Bach. Maybe I should read it again.

143

Today I was crossing the street by Patterson's and I saw Ralph, so I waited and walked with him to Howard's where we stood and talked about how we live, now we're alone. He does all his work, and I do all mine. He's ridding out things as I am. I told him about your roses, and he told me about Doris's antiques. He is so like you, in a certain shining, kind, intelligent way. I think I could like him very, very much. I, to end the conversation, suggested he have a cup of coffee with me some day, and he genially said "I'll do that." But, does he drink coffee?

I went on to the beauty shop and Lucile Mansfield was there. She asked for my telephone number for Harold, the high school boyfriend. She said he looked so serious when he told how disappointed he was because I didn't come to see him in the hospital. So what do I do now? It didn't work a long time ago.

My Bill is in Seattle visiting his son and family. I took him to the airport, August 13, and he looked so handsome, his wavy hair silver and longish, a white shirt and brown suit, the brown and green tie I brought him from London. I kissed him good-by and watched his plane carry him out of sight. He wrote about three fishing trips and how busy he'd been kept. I've thought about flying out and coming home with him, but perhaps I can get into more mischief here.

Honey, Lindbergh died this week in Hawaii, on Maui, where Bill's son and wife spent their vacation earlier. As Tennyson saith, "The old order changeth."

I must plan to visit Flossie Drage, about whom Florence is always talking. Her life must be very different, now that she is a widow, living alone in her parents' old home which she has renovated. She must be very pretty and very brave and very capable. I have heard so much about how beautifully she does things and how lovely she has decorated the house. It might be that I could get Lloyd to take me over to her house. He might want to stay and she might want him to. We who have so little time sometimes feel the urge to cling.

I bought a silver chest today for Bill, because he left me all Esther's silverware to polish while he was away, and he said he might buy a case for it. She had twelve of everything, even ice-tea spoons, Reed and Barton. That was one way of keeping me busy.

I don't know how my life will turn out. I only know I don't want

Bill hurt. I guess God is the manager, the One who is supposed to guard everyone's good. At times I am very much alone. Would I like it better otherwise? Bill is good and sweet and rugged, and he cares. Mostly we are comfortable together, but for keeps? I know whom I'd be so much more proud of, because he seems like you—but as he said today, things have a way of working out, and the wisest way is not to rush.

I keep remembering how you often said I was the most loved woman in Fort Wayne, and it helps me over some of my blue spots. You also told Nellie, and me too, that when you were dead I'd be the richest woman in Fort Wayne. It is convenient to feel I need never want. Charles Lamb said, "Competence to age is supplemental youth, a sorry supplement indeed, but I fear the best that is to be had." If I have supplemental youth, do I need supplemental love? Or just companionship?

I bought a new winter coat, nude cashmere, and it has style. For ten years I have wanted a good coat, but had to use my bronze all-weather coat, which wasn't too bad. I have a pretty rose and beige dress to start out with this fall, also beige shoes.

Oh, honey, clothes and people and relatives and clubs and church and organizations, and the house, and the money, and the plan for the rest of my life, an extension of yours, and then what have we? A rose-colored stone under the tree on the hill overlooking the valley of the newer cemetery. And then? As Browning said, "O thou soul of my soul, I shall clasp thee again, and with God be the rest!"

It has been three years and three months since you left me, and that is a long time, my dear—three years and three months!

October 16, 1974

Honey, it's just ten days until our thirtieth wedding anniversary. President and Mrs. Ford were wed in October, too— twenty-six years, yesterday. A lovely picture on television at 7:00 this morning, they were on the balcony overlooking the garden—she in blue—listening to a romantic song he had arranged for her. She's just home from the hospital after breast surgery.

I watched the lovely deep peach roses in the gold vase on a lacy yellow tablecloth at breakfast. They finally bloomed after being frosted last week. The placemats were flowery in the same color as the roses. Beginning the day with beauty, I was. Left the house at 8:20 for downtown in your Nova. It was such a beautiful sunny day but it had frosted again at thirty-one degrees. Gradually it became sixty-some, warm enough without a coat.

After parking across from the library, I went into the chapel. The sun was coming through the gold and blue and red window and casting pink, blue, and yellow shadows on the white wall. I sat in your place and thought a prayer. Then I went on to the Christian Women's prayer breakfast at the Shrine. Senator Hatfield's wife spoke. Had a piece of apple pie and coffee afterward at Ayres' and came home to my shows on thirty-three between one and two.

Thought about the two widows and a widower in the shows, and grabbing my camera, I hurried out to the cemetery. The leaves, I knew, would be beautiful and the entrance is so pretty. Took three pictures and came back. Road repairs were in progress on the Wayne Trace and on South Anthony, so I had to go on Tillman to the Decatur Road back to Paulding. Fixed the garbage cans, four of them, packed with leaves and marigolds that I had pulled. The front yard is brown again with locust twigs and leaves.

Had banana squash and ham for supper. Bill and I went north to see the trees last Wednesday and bought squash and cabbage and peppers. Stopped to see your folks. Mamie asked us back for supper, but we had steaks here.

Venetta came in last night with apples from Ethel's house. The larder is full, the checkbook balances, the car goes faster farther, the closets are full of clothes, and everything's going to be all right. But, oh, the awful ache in my heart, like last Monday when I was so lonely all day.

You haunt my memory like a song of long ago, and so I will live the fourth wedding anniversary, without you, on October 26. I will savor the sweetness of yesteryear, remember the present is all I have really, then trust and look up as I go toward my yonder.

January 28, 1975

Harry, the telephone just rang, "May I speak to Mr. Rahmer, please?" "Who's calling?" "A consumer research." So I explain and tell her I do not care to answer questions. I walk back into the study, eyes roaming the bookcase idly and stop at *As I Remember Him*. Always there will be reminders, and on a rainly night alone such reminders hang heavy.

Venetta and I just talked and made arrangements to go to Women's Club together to see a ninety-minute film on Austria, Thursday. We shared Austria, especially Vienna in 1971, you remember, shortly after you left.

I bought municipal bonds today, tax exempt and paying seven and one-half percent, $10,000 worth. Yesterday I had your name removed from $2,200 worth of my U.S. bonds. I am trying to get things in order always, it seems. How I wish you could help and enjoy the money, the work, the life!

I got through our wedding anniversary, Thanksgiving, and Christmas. Bill cooked a turkey for Thanksgiving and made a lettuce salad. I furnished pumpkin pie and whipped cream, and the cranberry sauce. A neighbor lady sent dressing. With our wine and coffee and bread and butter, it was super.

Christmas was super-super at Steve's house in Leo. He has a mustache now and seems so mature. Linda is sweet with Eric, Jamie, and baby Melissa. Danny was there, and Woodice looked so pretty even if her baby, Terra Maria, came on January 3. Torbin is a real boy at two years. Mamie and Mike, Woodie and Minnie, of course, were there. And you know the food!

Steve has been doing a lot of fixing on his house and it is very livable. And the tree! And the presents! I took nine pictures and every one was wonderful. So I sent sets of them to Mamie, Steve, Danny, and Shirley. Mamie and Mike are now in Arizona. And, honey, I gave each of the three nephews and Shirley a thousand-dollar check, as you once mentioned shortly before you left. It made me feel so good. Steve came after me and brought me back about 8:00.

I called Bill, and he wanted to come. I think he had been crying. Maybe next year I won't leave him alone at Christmas. The night before I had gone to Midnight Mass with Walt and Lucile and had breakfast with their friends afterward. Got home at 4:11, got up at 10:30 to dress for Steve's house. Bill is tender and sweet and human and easily hurt, but I couldn't take him to your folks at Christmas, though he's met many of them and though he was invited. It had to be just family.

Honey, I'm free, free, free! You know I've done everything you wanted me to, as far as I know, but get married. Yes, I would have married Ralph if he had asked me, but he took the woman second-house away. We've talked so much downtown and he's told me so many things, even about her. She was a widow for seventeen years, had a hard way to go, and he just got to thinking about it and thought, "Well, why not?" His appeal for me lay in the fact that he was so like you in so many ways, such a good, kindly man, a true gentleman.

It began last Christmas, our path-crossings, and it ended this past December 24 as I met him in the afternoon at Patterson's corner and walked with him to our church cater-corner by the library. We stood there and talked in the chill, and when he left he said, "I hope to see you again soon." So I went on to get my hair fixed, wondering if I would ever understand the feeling I have for him, or the way he looks at me. I am remembering a town, or place, we passed on our way to Denver—Last Chance.

I am remembering a poem, too, by Edward Rowland Sill, I think. A king's son had caused envy of his fine sword, and the craven threw his sword away in the sand. "Had I a sword like the king's son," he moaned. But later the king's son, wounded and sore and weaponless, saw the broken sword, hilt buried in the sand, and ran and grabbed it and with battle shout lifted afresh he hewed his enemy down, and saved a great cause that heroic day. And the craven had said, "But this blunt thing!" Maybe I am a craven about Bill. Sometimes I feel wicked, but I have to be very proud of a man—the man I marry—as proud as I was of you.

Your education, your appearance, your cleanliness, your fastidiousness about clothes, your gentleness and sweetness with me, your strong presence, and your pride appealed to me. Bill is more casual, is good company and good-natured, but he lacks the mind appeal and the magic touch. Again I feel wicked, but I looked up to you so. Remember how I used to tell you that "you were the best looking man there when we would leave a group or be at home again.

Oh, I know I found fault sometimes and said things I shouldn't. But I loved you true. As Ben Cartright said to Little Joe on TV when he was hurt because a girl died, "I'll tell you what Adam's grandfather said to me when Adam's mother died. 'Keep a soft spot for her in your heart, but don't carry her around on your back. She wouldn't want that.' "

I have a very soft spot for you, and I suppose Bill has for his wife. It is good we have the relationship we have, Bill and I.

Perhaps neither of us would like it for an all-time thing. So we're free, free.

I have had a month of not being quite up to par, the flu around the first of the year, three days when I could hardly get my legs to work, charley-horse like pains in the calves and hips. And a chest cold. Marvoline has been very ill, very weak, very despondent over the death of her last brother. It is not easy to get older alone.

Sunday Bill brought a dozen fish he had caught through the ice at the lake. They were delicious rolled in corn meal and fried in butter. I had made potato salad. Then we used fresh Riviera pears for salad or dessert. We had some of the burgundy his son recommended, too.

Oh, honey, I get along, I go a lot, but I just liked it better the way it was with you. In writing this, I am getting it all out, or is it a hopeless task? And am I old enough to know better? I do not live in a fantasy world. I do not even dream about you. I dream about school so much, and no pay. I wish the struggles of my dream schools would end and that I could feel more rested when I awake. Then maybe I could get over "what some call the laziness of grief," or the laziness of being alone. Anyway I want order in all my affairs, and I must work at it—before yonder.

Oh, I forgot to tell you about the French toast I had for supper tonight. It was the first time I fixed it since the last Saturday I fixed it for you as I usually did on a Saturday. I can still hear your "Thank you, thank you," as you always said it. So good, with plenty of syrup, pears, and coffee. Life is sweet sometimes.

Oh, yes, Walter and Lucile are floating around the world on the *Queen Elizabeth*. Marcia and I went to Muncie to see Sue's new baby, and Helen and I had lots of talking together, widows both. Marcia's Terry spent a month in Columbia, South America.

It would be so good to run to you, and hold you fiercely, and ask you questions and listen to your answers and tell you bits and bits and bits of news. And that the taxes are all done. The raindrops are falling against the windows. I must listen!

The telephone just rang. It was Phil to thank me for the pears I sent to him and Hope. Grace, Venetta, and I spent a glorious week end with Phil and Hope in Patriot, Indiana, on the Ohio River. They are both teaching in different schools, living in a big white house on a hill with the road, then the river, out front. The porch has square columns and the house is so attractively furnished in blues and reds. It was rainy but we went lots of places and ate out except for Sunday breakfast. It is raining harder here now. Get my hair fixed tomorrow.

April 23, 1975

Hi, Harry, I have just been glancing over my new *Travel* magazine, and it reminded me so of our trips over U.S.A., especially Denver and South Dakota. What wonderful times we had everywhere from Florida to California and in Kansas, too. Suddenly I warmed with the presence of you very near in this dear house. It was as if you were proud of your widow. Oh, you seem so close at times, and at other times so far, far away.

I wish you could see your precious little place with the new drapes in the back rooms and the lace cloth on the table with flowers and green twisted candles in silver. The little blue kitchen still has the splashy blue flowered curtains you chose, and the bed has the white quilted spread you purchased. There's a new orange and yellow and green rug under my feet, and I'm in the gold chair you used so much at the last. Oh, honey! The girls were here for bridge today. The dessert was "apple mystery," and before they left, some of them sat around the card table and copied the recipe from my *Farm Journal Cookbook*. And it rained all afternoon, but everyone had such a gay, good time.

The dishes are done and the chairs put back. Florence and I talked, and Bill called to see how things went and if we could be together tomorrow night.

It's spring. On Sunday after church I put my hands on the delicate branches by the steps and felt like Walt Whitman in "When I Heard the Learned Astronomer." The leaflets were so tiny, so fragile, so suggestive of God's planned universe. And one morning a red cardinal perched in the locust and checked me out. The very next morning a robin walked down the branch almost into the big window. The birthday bush, the roses, and the tulips are almost ready to start singing. And there will be lilacs in the dooryard across the way. You would love it all.

Mrs. Nahrwold came across to talk with me when I was playing pick-up in the back yard. She said Herm missed you, and we got really well acquainted after the winter in. She thought I had made such a wonderful adjustment. Oh, and is it ever an adjust-

150

ment to be without one who has been the dearest person you have ever known! She says Herm says the meanest things to her and Diane sometimes. That, I think, is one of life's greatest sorrows. If I could, I'd unsay every mean thing I ever said to you or anyone else. The record is there in a person's brain and it goes round and round. Of course, in our case, there was always the coming together in the common knowledge of a strong love, and as I said one criticizes most sorely when one cares the most. We both knew, I think, that there was an unshakable devotion. I am sorry about the chair that squeaked—Bill fixed it with your electric drill—it was broken.

Helen and Harold mowed their yard last night, and she worked with their roses. The black young couple back of me aren't very neat. Several neighbors have turned them in to environment control at the Board of Health, as I learned when I went down in person. I hope the summer isn't too unpleasant.

Honey, I'm going back to Europe for the fifth time, this time with the people I went to Mexico with—will visit Switzerland, the southern part of Germany where my father's people came from, Czeckoslovakia, and Austria. It will be great to be in Vienna and Zurich again. I will share a room with the Elizabeth I went to London with one January. The man I could have loved again will be along with his new wife. That knowledge, that knowledge, that I could have loved again, is good. There is nothing like having loved, so knowing that the glow could be again is something. Nothing is lost, all is experience, wisdom, God's share for the self.

To love again, maybe not. But to live again, that Bill has given me. Three years, the twenty-ninth of this month. The man-woman relationship has been both wonderful and exasperating for me, because I crave your genteel quanlities—in short, I make comparisons. Men have different ways with women. You were perfect in the way you loved, and that's the truth. I would like to love again the way I loved you, but I will take second best because it's better than none. Marriage, no. Now you know. There is so little time, or is there?

Harry, Cleon Fleck had surgery for cancer and now cobalt treatments. I went with Ruth to Lenten church suppers on his ticket four times. He was in the hospital then and she told me she couldn't bear to lose him. So many have gone like flowers in the frost, but new ones come on.

Roger's son, a senior in high school, had to be married in March.

It was a tormented time for Florence, and a concerned time for all of us. In July she will have three great grandchildren with Ken's two.

April 12, the day before Lloyd's birthday, I drove out and we went to Jon and Terry's new home, and then the four of us went to Poe for lunch. It was a delightful time and good to see a little new home where on the kitchen blackboard was written "I love you" and across the corner Jon had written "too." Such a gay, yellow kitchen with sweet yellow flowered curtains and hanging flowerpots with real vines. There's an upstairs, and a basement, and a big garage. A big back yard with trees, too.

Walter and Lucile are home now and the three of us went out to eat at the K. of C. Last year the three of us went to the Credit Union meeting and I won fifty dollars in a drawing. This year I drove out alone in the dark to Wayne High School and won fifty dollars again.

The car is sounding like it has a lot of little chickens under the hood and I've a date to have it checked at the garage. No one at the filling station seems to know why, and I did go back to the garage without learning why—Les used an oil additive and said it would ease out. This time I'm going out driving with the manager. It started right after I had the car inspected as I drove out on Werling Road. One wonders if they wronged me for some peculiar reason.

Tomorrow is the last meeting of the Women's Club, except for the May breakfast. I am taking Roger Wattercutter's wife as my guest. He is the new I.D.S. man I bought municipal bonds from, did I tell you? He is thirty-three, she is thirty. They took me to dinner at Holly's Landing last week. He's a lot like my nephew Roger, and she's like someone I've always known. It's so easy for me to like young people, probably because of my juniors and seniors in high school teaching.

Marvoline is better and we spent a delightful day at church, and at lunch at The Wharf a couple Sundays ago. Had delicious fish, salad from the bar, fresh homemade bread, and rosé wine, plenty of it. We talked long and walked all around the Times Corner shopping area. She made a pretty pink dress to put her mother-in-law away in—pink was Ada's favorite color. Now there are three graves across Lake Wawasee, and Marvoline will be alone in the green cottage, very much alone since her two brothers have gone, Ed, and his folks. Some flowers linger longer in the frost.

Freida finally made the brown dress from the material I bought in St. Thomas last June. Venetta and I and her mother went to Grabill where we met Freida for lunch, and then back to her house while she sewed. I wore it Easter to church and to Bill's house for supper. Florence and Ken enjoyed Bill's pork loin roast with apples, mashed potatoes, and lettuce and tomato salad. I took deviled eggs and the apple pie Bill ordered. Afterward we played continental rum.

We were at Florence and Ken's one night when Ken's brother was in town, and was he ever a hippie man, smelly and all, and all. Today she brought a picture he sent of his second family, a Spanish wife who teaches Spanish at the university in Gainsville, and three teenagers. In the picture they all look so fine. Of course one son has long hair to his elbows, parted in the center, but there still is a good, clean, intelligent appearance. Ken's brother lived in Venezuela much of his life, is now retired, and is working to settle his father's estate, part of which is a 640-acre farm in the southwest corner of North Dakota.

Oh, my darling, there is so much going on. I wish I could run to your arms and put my head against your shoulder and snuggle where there would be no need for words. Yet how many things I wish we had talked about! People do not always find time for the encouraging word, the comforting word, the heart-to-heart word.

Somewhere I read that a mantle of grief could become a garland of roses. Perhaps later I will remember where I read it. I read so much. That is a beautiful thought and quite an extravagant transformation, from grief to roses. It brings to mind a line from a song, "I came into the garden while the dew was still on the roses."

There is thunder outside and raindrops sound against the window. I must be beautiful tomorrow in blue, almost the color of my wedding dress, and I must stand and introduce my young guest. So it is good-by, good-by, good-by, this night.

May 12, 1975

Harry, it is mid-spring and it is raining again. Of the dozen cerise tulips with lily-like petals that you planted and which bloomed so gorgeously that May four years ago, only one now stands with bowed head, but it has points that reach out. Life must be like that for me, reaching, though it is so wonderful to curl in and coil sometimes, with someone you love.

In church yesterday I thought so much about you as I sat alone at the end of a seat for five, and an older woman sat at the other end. But I had given Terry and Marcia a driving lesson at 8:30. They are going to Spain for three weeks and have inquired about a car there with a stick shift. So twice I, who am certainly not an expert, have helped them. The car works much better now, no little chickens chirping anymore. And also, I had attended the most wonderful book review on *Lion Country*, by Frederick Buechner. It is not about lions, but about a wonderfully strange evangelist who faces the world's dangers, and it was given by a very vital young woman who made me want to read everything the author wrote. I picked up two friends on the way in to church and we picked up two more to have coffee together while we listened to the review. Afterward, I simply went my own way to the eleven o'clock service as I so often do. I thought so much in church, and I wondered why I didn't get busy and write your story. This is, more or less, my story.

Honey, I worked three days in the yard last week, mowing, killing dandelions, planting flowers, chopping sod. Then on Saturday I worked at cleaning the house. It is so good to see progress. The air was clear and warm, almost like that May morning when you left, and there were gentle breezes. The trees are so gently green, and the yellow forsythia, mauve magnolias, red tulips, and white cherry blossoms sing and sing.

Bill and I went hunting for mushrooms in a woods near Dad's old farm and we found enough to brown in butter for our steaks Tuesday. Bill was here last night and I baked a strawberry pie. We each ate two pieces with ice cream and coffee. I had pan broiled the steaks because the pie ran over in the oven at the last moment or two. There was good fresh whole wheat bread and slivered green beans with canned mushrooms. It is so pleasant to have a man to cook for and to eat with. He took me to the M.C.L. for supper one day last week.

I don't think he feels too well and he has gone back to smoking. And Mr. N., honey, he is something else. Mrs. N. told me last week he can't find his way home in the car, even in the neighborhood, and he accuses her of such awful things. The doctor said he wasn't responsible enough to hold a job or to take a trip, maybe to Hawaii. I am so glad you didn't have to become like that, for your sake as well as mine. Oh, I hope, more than anything else, that my mind and my memory stay sharp and keen till the last!

In a little while I will get ready to go to Lucile's to join friends who will see her pictures taken on her "around the world" trip—not all of them, she says. It should be a pleasant afternoon.

Her little house is quite surrounded with black people, and yesterday young Africans were on parade past the Baxter side of our little house. Bare backs glistened from the summer clothes, and the Sunday attire wasn't too bad. It isn't the black I mind, it's the trashy "see me" attire there sometimes is, and it's the trashy brown sacked garbage that sits across the back alley, sacks open at the top and sacks that will melt in the rain. Lucile and I have lived in our little houses for more than twenty-five years and, like you and Walt, they are part of us. Yet life is a changing process, and I may have to give up the house as well as you and become a sort of alien, a foreigner in a foreign land.

Honey, Roger's son's wife lost her baby at six months, and they gave the body to science as the doctor and minister suggested. After all the adjustments of a hurry-up marriage, and the new mother-to-be quitting high school, and the setting up of an apartment home, this other adjustment.

As long as I lived with you, no matter what the trouble, life had an aura, a romantic rose-colored aura where I was comfortable and cozy, and perhaps without knowing it somewhat self-centered. Now I see and think of others more, and I understand Helen Lee's realistic harshness. The world is fraught with dangers and unpleasant situations, and we do not always bring them upon ourselves. And sometimes we can wonder "Where is God?" Last night I watched on TV the tragic life and execution of the Russian royal family in 1917, and there have been so many tragic pictures of refugees from Cambodia and Viet Nam. How would I feel in certain positions, were I certain people?

I suppose, after four years, it is graduation time, commencement time. I suppose I wish I could tell you I have a new house and a new man and a new as-happy life. Perhaps I am a failure. But I have learned much as a widow. Life does have to go on, and laughter does bounce back. Lilacs do bloom again. The under-current of sorrow and loss is ever-present, but so is the sweetness

of memories of a shared life. One balances the books, one faces
the facts of the loss and one bears the added work and the renewed
vision of the world from where you are to where everything else
is, and you choose faith and courage.

Always, always, you can reach for the romance of living, and
you can remember the roses. What beautiful words begin with
'r,' Mr. Rahmer! But what riches if I could say "I love you" and
hear you echo "I love you too, Irene."

March 15, 1976

Oh, Harry, you have really been on my mind a lot for the past
two weeks, and when I re-read the last note to you and saw the
date was May 12, 1975, I knew I had much more to tell you, even
if I did decide once to stop then. Almost a year. And another
springtime. And five years soon will have gone by.

Beautiful May time, the time in 1940 when we knew the wild
sweetness of love one night, and I took myself to church the next
day, overwhelmed with a dream that was to come true. Blessed
was I among women as my 'thank-you, God's' raced through my
mind in spite of the music and the sermon and the prayers. And
then lovely May each year as we finished our teaching work and
enjoyed the house and the leisure and the roses.

Sad, sad May, five years ago, when you finished your life and
left me the house, the leisure, the roses. And oh, so much
more—unshed tears, and fears and drears come to my thoughts.
But I have survived, I am stronger.

The word "widow" rankles me. She doesn't fit in with couples,
or unmarrieds, and she doesn't want to court other widows. I am
at home with young people, and I do have Bill. I keep moving,
and I cultivate independence. The 'twos' make their own little
world and together they can face anything, only they don't always
know it.

I went out to your place on the little hill two weeks ago, first
time since October, and then I drove out north to Concordia College by way of Reed Road. Should I be living on Reed Road instead
of Reed Street? And I thought of Marvoline's house. Should I have
bought it? But I liked mine better, even if hers is in a better area.
Honey, she's dead too. Was found on the floor in her living room,
telephone off the hook, lights on. You and Ed and she. I, left alone.
Times the four of us were together leap into my mind at times,

156

we four at a table at Columbia City and again at the Gas House, and at church, and here, and there. The three of you so quickly left life, at fifty-seven, sixty-two, seventy.

The story rambles. Black people moved into Nagel's house, the pretty red-gabled place directly in front of our place. I was eating lunch, looked up, saw a shiny yellow Cadillac, then a truck which they proceeded to unload. The davenport is white and the bedroom furniture Mediterranean. The man has a goatee and is young. The little boy carried his load in proudly.

I drove to Mike's Car Wash and had my Nova made clean and shiny. A week before a real estate lady called me for my house and said she had just sold to blacks on my street. She would help me find a new home. I have since talked to neighbors and they say they are not going to let it influence them.

Oh, honey, I went to Switzerland, Germany, Czechoslovakia, and Austria in the summer with some of the people I went to Mexico with in 1973. It was so lovely, so very beautiful. The Black Forest, the flowering window boxes, the mountains, the rivers, the quaint and the modern cities, yes, and the weinersnitzel and the white wine. I walked and walked in Vienna, in the park in front of the Intercontinental, down toward St. Steven's Cathedral and through the city. Elizabeth doesn't care to walk as much as I. I looked in the telephone book and found Bill's father's and mother's family names. I bought things for Bill. He especially likes the salt and pepper shakers with the Lippizan horses on them.

In St. Moritz, Elizabeth and I went to a new Catholic church and listened to the most beautiful voices singing German hymns. We could follow the words, and marvel at the voices riding the notes so easily. On the way back to our hotel, we stopped for pastries and coffee. Again it was glorious, being there in such different surroundings. Salzburg, and Innsburck, and Grindlewald. How happy we were the three days at the latter town! And then Lucerne, and the lake from our balcony at night. And Zurich, and the big plane home after three weeks. I was rather glad Ralph and his new wife were not along.

I was home only a little while when Freida called. Would I go to Australia with her in November? During our phone conversation I made up my mind. It was one of the greatest things I ever did. I rounded out my summer clothes with new camel-colored shoes and purse and bought a beige and brown raincoat. It was raining the Sunday I left, and I was blue for you. Freida's sister and husband took me to the airport on November 2. Chicago, then L.A., where we had to wait about four hours and our group got together, twenty-three of us. To Hawaii, then Auckland. Memories swell up and surround me as I think of Rotorua, Christchurch, Sydney. We lost the couple from Kentucky here, because he had a heart attack. It was springtime in Sydney, and the strawberries were ripe, the flowers in bloom.

The tiniest airport at Mt. Cook, and the tiniest airplane took four passengers up to the glacier. Walking in snow and on ice we were, when minutes before we were too warm!

I bought an opal ring, and an opal pin for Florence in Melbourne. The guide helped me choose them. Of Russian parentage, Ivan of the bushy blond hair and the ruddy kewpie face is a whole story. In Tasmania we stayed at Launceston and at Hobart. It was all less primitive than I had thought. The food was excellent, the hotels also, the land was dotted with sheep and cattle feeding. And the flowers, especially the roses! You would have loved it!

The train from Adelaide to Perth was an experience, two night's sleep on a train, three days filled with experiences. I found the sweetest baby, Catherine, in the lounge car. Her young parents let me hold her. Ruth Lowery snapped my picture with the baby and put it in my Christmas card. Perth was aglow with purple jacaranda, and I loved walking from the hotel down into the city. Bought my Christmas cards there. Also I found a nice doctor lady who took the hardened wax out of my ear. I had gone deaf in one ear on the train the way I did a few days before we were to be married. But before I went to her, I had my hair fixed. It was November 27, Thanksgiving. Our guide planned an American Thanksgiving for us at the hotel with two turkeys, pumpkin pie, fruit cocktail, and all the wine we wanted, not to mention vegetables and salad. Perth was perfect. I was very happy there.

We flew back to Adelaide and went up through the Barossa Valley, on to Ayers Rock and Alice Springs. All in all, I think we were on twenty-three different planes. I mentioned my ear trouble. When I arrived in Aukland, I had swollen ankles that finally got back to normal with walking. During the first week I got sick and vomited awful one afternoon and evening. All the time I had constipation and had to take laxatives. No one but Freida saw me sick, but on the plane from Alice Springs to Cairns many vomited. At the halfway stop, three were stretched out on seats at the airport. Thirty-eight days is a long time, and some of the trip was rugged in a way, but it still was wonderful, wonderful!

Cairns was a tropical area, so was Figi. Freida and I had to stay over at L.A. because of a United Airline Strike. We finally came home T.W.A. to Dayton, to Indianapolis, and Delta from there to here. There was four inches of snow on the ground in Fort Wayne, after all the beautiful extra spring and some summer.

And, Harry, I spent Christmas at Danny's again, near Angola. Woodie and Minnie came to get me and brought me home in a snow storm. Later there was an ice storm and more snow. The ground was covered and we were nearly frozen in place until mid-February, when It became unseasonably warm.

I am so thankful for health and wealth. I think if I could have you I would be far too happy. Bill and I are going along in about the same way. Harry, I wonder If you can understand that it is good we have each other, since we can't have you and Esther. But you were the most understanding person I have ever known. It was part of your equipment as a teacher. I could be utterly free with you. I could take anything to you.

Tomorrow a minister of our church, Mr. Scott, is going to review *A Month of Sundays*, by John Updike, for the Women's Club after a luncheon. I have read it. The part about this degenerate minister in the book visiting his father in a nursing home made me think a lot. Also the part about sex. I can think of a lot of things some would call degenerate—one garners much on many subjects if he is awake during a lifetime. And the part on death. "And for the living, how acceptable the death of the dead, how quickly the place seals over where they were, how slyly grateful we are for the little extra space they bequeath us! We would abhor them were they to return. One of our profoundest fears, indeed, is that the dead will return."

Return in memory, yes. Maybe I am somewhat abnormal. Maybe I don't try hard enough to forget, but should I? I have taken over in this house, but I'd be happier sharing it, or another, with you. I drive your car with far greater ease, but I'd be happier seated right of the driver. I use your money for travel, but I also gave some of it to your sisters' children. I keep still about you to others.

I think I'll go to the kitchen and eat a grapefruit. Remember how we savored them in the old days. We savored so many things together. Life is so wonderful, every day to be savored—the end will come.

July 4, 1976

Hi, Harry, I didn't go to church at ten o'clock. I waived it in place of watering the roses and all the flowers—even reset some little volunteers I found. It is seventy-one degrees and ten till ten—no rain prophesied until Thursday. Sweat is dropping off my neck in back—I hope I don't ruin my hair-do. It has to last a while.

I have thought of you so many, many times. I was blue all through May, and then in June I faced reality. It's the hospital for me tomorrow at 2:00 p.m. The tumor we knew I had is bigger, three pounds or more. My doctor and your doctor and Florence's doctor checked me. Sometimes I feel as if a little kangaroo got into my pouch in Australia. Anyway I hate to go through with it, but I know I can't wait any longer. It is a miserable, full feeling. Otherwise I am fine, fine, fine.

It will be the first time you haven't leaned over to kiss me as when I went to other surgeries. I won't see you watching and waiting for me to be well again. I will have Bill and Florence.

Yesterday I drove to the bank at Hoagland and to Lloyd's and Marilyn's. On the way back I stopped at the low hill by the tree that was once a sapling. Stood by the car in its wide, cool shade and read and re-read our names on the pink stone with the roses. Somehow a strange peace pervaded my soul, and I drove away for a new toaster at the M & M Store, and to clean my house.

The outside is perfect. Bill trimmed the hedge Thursday. I mowed and trimmed the bushes and tended the flowers. I had taken the bedclothes all to the laundry, and yesterday I did all my personal wash. If people have to come in, it won't be too bad.

But the people, when they do come, soon, or later, won't know how it really was with us. They won't understand the sweat and tears and love and fears, and the glory and success of our winning our M.A. degrees together, and the love of teaching we knew as we graded our math and English papers at night after days challenging and satisfying with young people. The thank-yous, sometimes unsaid, but nevertheless there, in smiles, in thoughtful

160

young eyes, were the best pay. It was a beautiful life, but over again, I'd make it so very beautiful.

They, the people who must come in somehow, they wouldn't understand the handwork on the household linens, many of them made in sewing club with longtime friends. They wouldn't know, really know, your love of roses. Roses are on our dishes and on our silverware. The treasures people love aren't treasured so by outsiders. Then our books we loved, who would care? I'm thinking of the song "God, Bless This House." It was filled with love, as was that first apartment in the treetops. And how much you helped me with the cleaning and the sweetness of this home!

No one will understand our money, and those first plans and the extra work to gain a foothold. And the joy of our trips together! How many, many couples waste the joy they might have found together wisely! The Murphy divorce is final after the third try. Life is such a vital, ever-changing thing, and I love it, especially now—when I might not have it much longer. (I must go change the hose again.)

The salvias will be taller when I come home from the hospital. The car is freshly washed at the Mike Car Wash. How I love it and even love to drive it! The house windows were freshly washed Thursday. Oh, how I hope everything goes well! There are new bing cherries in the refrigerator and also a hunk of watermelon. And it's almost time to eat again.

Bill was here last night, and he will bring chicken tonight. With what I have to finish up, we will have a good supper. There will be peach melbas for dessert. Florence will take me to the hospital tomorrow. She and Lloyd have keys to the house and garage. Right now, she is to get a third, Lloyd a third, and your three nephews and Shirley a third. That is after $5,000 out for the church. There must be nearly half a million. How rich we were, every way you take it! And I guess, as Lloyd said, we just lease it while we live. It's God's, and we mustn't forget the government. Would that that were God's!

August 29, 1976

Oh, Harry, I am brimming with happiness. It's so strange to think I'd ever feel this way. There is something in Isaiah that speaks of the oil of gladness for those who mourn, and a mantle of praise instead of a faint heart. One thing, and one only, you, would make me perfectly joyous. Yet, how full and complete I feel, having been loved by you, and loving so. But today must be what counts.

I went to church, the farthest I have driven since the operation. It was sunny and pleasant as I went into the chapel, and the glory of being there alone in your seat almost overwhelmed me. The blues and reds of the window were radiant, and if ever I felt close to God, it was there, and my heart sang with praise after praise in the rays of beauty that seemed to wrap me. On either side of the altar were yellow gladiolas—yellow, in the center of every flower, in every star, in the sun and moon—a glorious color.

A minister from New Haven Presbyterian held the service. Afterward I drove to MacDonald's for a quarter pounder with cheese and a chocolate malted. Thought of going to our place on the hill, but Bill took me out there just before he left for Seattle to be with his son and family.

At home I tried on dresses, and surprise! I can wear all the ones I couldn't before surgery. I am ten pounds lighter. I have too many dresses and things, I am rich, rich, rich.

This has really been a week. On Monday the doctor gave me permission to take steps, to sweep, to drive the car. I am healed fine inside, and he is proud of my nice scar, almost hip-to-hip across by belly. In another month, by the last of September, I can do anything I ever did—but until then, no heavy lifting or moving the furniture.

Bill was here four nights before he left on Wednesday. How good it was to be with him that last night, to feel like a real woman again! Venetta says I love him, but I am wary about marriage. I told him once this week I didn't love him, and I also told him I'd have married him five years ago if he hadn't smoked so much, and he said he wouldn't like that because I would be too happy. There you are. However, I believe the greatest happiness in life is that between a man and woman who can enjoy with wisdom and tolerance.

Oh, Harry, the operation was not easy, and yet because I knew it had to be, I went along with it. Instead of your nearness and tenderness, Florence rushed out of the room when the trailer-cot came. A little black nurse greeted me at surgery with, "I've got you now, Mrs. Rahmer." I had taught her, and called her this time by her sister's name. Got the family anyway. I had taught four of them. Little Helen Culpher. So many other nurses, and the doctor, and the anaesthesiologist, all under the big dome. I had seen operation drama on television often, but the needle was so soon into my arm.

Back in my room, there was Florence. I thought she must be going deaf—she kept saying she couldn't hear me, and I thought she ought to. She came every day. So did Venetta on the way to lunch or to her car after work. The doctor came every day. Marcia came. There were flowers and cards and people from the church.

The nurses were all nice, but they made me do all I could. Took my blood pressure, temperature, checked my pad for bleeding, watched the catheter, gave me shots and pills. The food, so awful at first, got better and better. I asked for an extra day, and could hardly stand to stay the night. Home on July 14 at two o'clock, nine days.

Florence shopped for me. Bill began coming, he had been at the hospital two nights. Helen and Mrs. Nahrwold came. There's so much you see to do and can't. My scar at first looked like Jimmy Carter's smile, the reason several people got to see it. I have three up-and-down ones plus this new across one, have been well operated on. But one's toenails grow, and you wonder how you'll ever get at them without tearing open the scar. Bill offered, but one day after a bath, I got it done, tremblingly. Your hair gets greasy, and Florence took me to a beauty shop after two weeks and two days. It was all right, and I wanted to eat lunch out, but I could barely walk to the car afterward.

Bill and I fixed supper here that evening, watched the Olympic games, and when he went home, I decided, after all, to do the dishes. A great gob of blood ran down my legs. I washed and padded and wondered and then finished the dishes. Had I ruined myself?

Everything you think you want is in the basement or the attic, but you can't go there. Florence hung up the wash I did. The bed needed changing, and I couldn't lift the mattress, so Bill helped with that. Nahrwold mowed the lawn, Helen edged the flower beds. Weeds grow, dead flowers collect on the bushes. You want to pull and cut, but you can't yet.

Oh, how thrilled I was when some of the women took me to the Lamp Post, and to the McKinnie Tap for dinner. Venetta and I went to the Dutch Mill this week with her aunt. Florence and I

163

went to the beauty shop twice and ate out. When I could go down-town on the bus, I was so happy, and I ate at Ayres'. It was both a good and an awkward situation. Bill brought supper in, and once we ate out this week.

His son came the 9th of August with his family. There was a salmon cook-out at Bill's home the 10th. I took cookies baked from Bill's sister's recipe, and the three little black-haired, brown-eyed girls, eight, ten, and twelve liked them enormously. Julie is thin-ner and so friendly. Neighbors were there. Salmon, corn on the cob, baked potatoes, sliced tomatoes were the main course. One of the ladies brought an angel food confetti cake for dessert, there was coffee, and my cookies. Young Bill saw that everyone had white wine while the food was cooking.

The following Saturday night was family night, and what a time I had with them! Took more cookies, and angel cake, and a fruit salad with blueberries, peaches, bananas, and mandarin oranges. Bill fixed a pork roast. His son wanted corn again. Po-tatoes and apples were cooked along with the roast in my roaster. Took pictures. It was good to visit with young Bill. Class president in his sophomore and senior years, he and I, as the sponsor, spent much time together. How I adored him then and relied on him. He had a way with the students. The three girls put on Olympic stunts, and did some dances in the yard while we older folks sat and talked on the patio by the back porch.

Yesterday and the day before I swept the carpet and scrubbed the linoleum in the bath and kitchen—first time in eight weeks. Such joy to be able to do my house leisurely and safely! No wonder I feel so good. It is wonderful to have this operation behind me. I see that with it, there were many really bright spots. "Checkered shade and sunshine," as Longfellow said of life. Oh, if you could hold me and I could cling, but I have to stand alone. And your love, the memory of it, helps me to stand tall.

I have read so many wonderful books that helped. *Upon This Rock*, by Frank G. Slaughter, was about Peter in Bible times. *Miracle of the Bells*, by Janney, I read because you had once said in such a thoughtful way, as you laid it down, was a beautiful story. About death. Those two books before the surgery. At home I tackled the condensed books, not *Reader's Digest*, in my set for the years 1953-57, those years when I was class sponsor and when Mother died and I spent so much time with Father, when I didn't have much time to read. I had you and my home and my teaching. How busy we were! And we had begun to take time to travel in U.S.A. How happy people sometimes are without fully realizing it! Good heavens! I had surgery in '51, '52, and '53. And I worked on the *Journal Gazette* in '53, the summer I had surgery for two tumors on my right leg. No wonder we skipped the books then. But I found so much that interested me, stories I understood and appreciated better for having been there, in Australia, New Zealand, and Figi, the locale of some of the stories.

It's such fun living. I hate to think of being old and leaving the world. I wonder about you. What is it really like, being dead?

The flowers have never been prettier. My back yard and Helen's are a lovely rendezvous, with yellow marigolds predominating. We talk so much since she has retired. At the east side of the house I have a bi-centennial bed, red salvia, white periwinkle, and blue browallia. A huge bank of three feet high orange and yellow marigolds hems in the house and hedge at the northeast corner. A bed of coral impatiens is at that end of the north side. Burgundy and orange marigolds are at the south side. Roses and impatiens and lantana are in front. My blue verbenas by the back fence were so lovely. Red zinnias were in the fence corner and salvia all along the fence. Delphinium is by the garage still, and tiny yellow marigolds line the garage, both sides. But oh, the roses you raised, so very, very beautiful. I try. Some of yours are still blooming, and Bill and I have added new ones, but they don't produce as yours did. And those tulips of that Maytime in 1971 have about dwindled out. Still, the place has been very colorful, and I'm glad I worked as hard as I did before going to the hospital.

Oh, I was on the same floor you were there, and I walked past the Room 509 several times and lived it all over. How far I've come since those first faltering steps after surgery! And since those first faltering steps without you.

October 18, 1976

Harry, I've just come from my Presbyterian Woman's Group supper with Edna Chester. It's 8:30. I sat with Marjorie Perry, whose husband, a lawyer, is going through what you did with your coronary occlusion. He's sixty now, two years after his troubles, and wants to retire. He's very angry, short-fused, and it's difficult for her. She told how sad I looked when she first knew me, about five years ago, but she always thought I was pretty. She is pretty, too. The wife bears the hurt, too, the agony, the loneliness, the apprehension. They had no children either. Ah, yes, she was a teacher, and teachers have so many and such varied children. Like Mr. Chips, we have had thousands in our ninety years of teaching together.

Bill came in the evening. He has a new red Brick, rather the color is bitter-sweet, and it's the biggest Buick made in 1975. He bought it from his son when he was in Seattle. He and a Lincoln Life man drove it home, with the latter's wife and son and daughter, little ones. It is lovely, and Bill is a comfort and a care, in a way. I should take what God giveth and be happier, but Sir, I loved and can love only you. I wish I could be a merry widow and dance away. I wish I could sing and shout to the high heavens. I wish I could love again! It is not enough to be loved. That's only half the cake. And I want it all with icing piled high.

Helen's and my lovely garden flowers were frosted last night by the twenty-some degrees. I felt a sadness today, walking by them. Oh, the purple mums, and some of the roses are not so bad as the golden marigolds and red salvia. "A cold wind came out of the north, chilling and killing my Annabel Lee."

Some pretty words were found in my sewing box today as I cleaned it. "After all, a high station in life is earned by the gallantry with which appalling experiences are survived with grace." Also "pride is a necessity of survival with honor." Down below, in the clipping, I saw "Make voyages, attempt them, there's nothing else."

Pretty words in print, and beauty anywhere, have always meant so much to me. You shared that love of good reading and the beauty of life with me. Love glistens the world for two, a man and a maid. Without that I must go a-voyaging.

Elizabeth and I talk often of our coming trip to South America, November 6 through 27. Oh, I pray it is a safe, a happy trip. And coming back home will be a delightful lull, a time to re-assess, and a prelude to Christmas. The lights you decked our place with are all gone, given away. I used to love to beat you home from school and have them glowiing with greeting to you when you came home. Joy to the world, our world!

I washed all the windows, took out the storms, did them in the kitchen this time. Did I say all? Yes, all but the bathroom one and the kitchen ones. In two days I had done that and also mowed the grass for the first time since my surgery. Of course the front lawn had to be raked for the leaves from the locust tree. Five garbage cans and two big sacks full of refuse. It felt so good to be strong and well again! Yes, the two doors were cleaned too.

Bill and I drove to Defiance in his Buick the second Sunday after he came home. Strange, your and his people from that town, and you and he both born in March. His sister's new friend in ninety in May. Think of it! He is so alert, has traveled, lived in Florida, been married twice, the last time to a school teacher. That makes him nineteen years older than she. He took us to the Holiday Inn at Napoleon, Ohio, for dinner, and it was super. Came back to his home, then to Christine's. Brought half a pumpkin pie home that she had baked.

Florence and I are going to a prayer breakfast at the Shrine tomorrow at 8:30. It may snow tonight, according to the forecast, so we decide how we get there in the morning.

Driving the car is becoming something of a joy. Am working on 7,000 miles. Must get it winterized before I leave. Also it needs an oil change and to be lubricated. The furnace needs checking. I think about the roof sometimes, and the basement windows. Your chair needs to be replaced. It's difficult to see to everything.

Election time is coming up; Carter or Ford? I should like to talk it over with you before I vote. Shirley wants my mother's picture, the big one when she was seventeen. The glass needs to be replaced. I should look over the photos and perhaps pass some of them on. And the books that were so precious, perhaps I should weed them out. The stuff in the basement I keep working on. And there's the attic stuff. Honey, there are the strangest sounds in this house, have been ever since you were away. They don't scare me, but they make me wonder.

I sew sometimes. Made two dresses longer. I can wear some that were hanging back because I now have a waist line and a ten-pound loss in weight. It's a joy to be attractive, a quiet pride when I go places. Oh, Harry, I hope I stay pretty awhile, get things done I should, and that my mind and senses last as long as I.

I want to keep remembering the roses. There's a huge vase of them on the dinette table and a single flaming peace rose in a black vase in the kitchen. I picked the buds so they wouldn't get frosted. They keep blooming inside, the last roses of summer.

When I lived upstairs in rooms or in apartments, I used to long for a bit of earth to raise flowers in, and then I found you and you gave me roses, all kinds of roses, and you arranged them in bouquets. At the table there was always the fragrance and beauty of roses, and when they were frosted, I brought out the candle holders and candles to give grace to our winter suppers. Ah, we two!

Truly, then my cup runneth over. Though since then I have walked through the valley of the shadow, I have also frolicked in green pastures beside still waters. And, moreover, I have been followed by goodness and mercy. Goodnight, Harry. "Goodnight, Irene!"